D1272993

Introduction to Free Radical Chemistry

Prentice-Hall Foundations of Modern Organic Chemistry Series

KENNETH L. RINEHART, JR., Editor

Volumes published or in preparation

N. L. ALLINGER and J. ALLINGER	**STRUCTURES OF ORGANIC MOLECULES**
TRAHANOVSKY	**FUNCTIONAL GROUPS IN ORGANIC COMPOUNDS**
STEWART	**THE INVESTIGATION OF ORGANIC REACTIONS**
SAUNDERS	**IONIC ALIPHATIC REACTIONS**
GUTSCHE	**CHEMISTRY OF CARBONYL COMPOUNDS**
PRYOR	**INTRODUCTION TO FREE RADICAL CHEMISTRY**
STOCK	**AROMATIC SUBSTITUTION REACTIONS**
RINEHART	**OXIDATION AND REDUCTION OF ORGANIC COMPOUNDS**
DEPUY	**MOLECULAR REACTIONS AND PHOTOCHEMISTRY**
IRELAND	**ORGANIC SYNTHESIS**
DYER	**APPLICATIONS OF ABSORPTION SPECTROSCOPY OF ORGANIC COMPOUNDS**
BATES and SCHAEFER	**RESEARCH IN ORGANIC CHEMISTRY**
TAYLOR	**HETEROCYCLIC COMPOUNDS**
HILL	**COMPOUNDS OF NATURE**
BARKER	**ORGANIC CHEMISTRY OF BIOLOGICAL COMPOUNDS**
STILLE	**INDUSTRIAL ORGANIC CHEMISTRY**
RINEHART and SIM	**X-RAY CRYSTALLOGRAPHY AND MASS SPECTROMETRY OF ORGANIC COMPOUNDS**
BATTISTE	**NON-BENZENOID AROMATIC COMPOUNDS**

INTRODUCTION TO FREE RADICAL CHEMISTRY

William A. Pryor

Associate Professor of Chemistry
Louisiana State University

PRENTICE-HALL, INC., ENGLEWOOD CLIFFS, N.J.

Library of Congress Catalog Card Number 66-12785
Printed in the United States of America
C-48415(p)
C-48416(c)

PRENTICE-HALL INTERNATIONAL, INC., London
PRENTICE-HALL OF AUSTRALIA PTY. LTD., Sydney
PRENTICE-HALL OF CANADA, LTD., Toronto
PRENTICE-HALL OF INDIA (PRIVATE) LTD., New Delhi
PRENTICE-HALL OF JAPAN, INC., Tokyo

Current Printing (last digit):
10 9 8 7 6 5 4 3 2 1

To the TP

Foreword

Organic chemistry today is a rapidly changing subject whose almost frenetic activity is attested by the countless research papers appearing in established and new journals and by the proliferation of monographs and reviews on all aspects of the field. This expansion of knowledge poses pedagogical problems; it is difficult for a single organic chemist to be cognizant of developments over the whole field and probably no one or pair of chemists can honestly claim expertise or even competence in all the important areas of the subject.

Yet the same rapid expansion of knowledge—in theoretical organic chemistry, in stereochemistry, in reaction mechanisms, in complex organic structures, in the application of physical methods—provides a remarkable opportunity for the teacher of organic chemistry to present the subject as it really is, an active field of research in which new answers are currently being sought and found.

To take advantage of recent developments in organic chemistry and to provide an authoritative treatment of the subject at an undergraduate level, the *Foundations of Modern Organic Chemistry Series* has been established. The series consists of a number of short, authoritative books, each written at an elementary level but in depth by an organic chemistry teacher active in research and familiar with the subject of the volume. Most of the authors have published research papers in the fields on which they are writing. The books will present the topics according to current knowledge of the field, and individual volumes will be revised as often as necessary to take account of subsequent developments.

The basic organization of the series is according to reaction type, rather than along the more classical lines of compound class. The first ten volumes in the series constitute a core of the material covered in nearly every one-year organic chemistry course. Of these ten, the first three are a general introduction to organic chemistry and provide a background for the next six, which deal with specific types of reactions and may be covered in any order. Each of the reaction types is presented from an elementary viewpoint, but in a depth not possible in conventional textbooks. The teacher can decide how much of a volume to cover. The tenth examines the problem of organic synthesis, employing and tying together the reactions previously studied.

The remaining volumes provide for the enormous flexibility of the series. These cover topics which are important to students of organic chemistry and are sometimes treated in the first organic course, sometimes in an intermediate course. Some teachers will wish to cover a number of these books in the one-year course; others will wish to assign some of them as outside reading; a complete intermediate organic course could be based on the eight "topics" texts taken together.

The series approach to undergraduate organic chemistry offers then the considerable advantage of an authoritative treatment by teachers active in research, of frequent revision of the most active areas, of a treatment in depth of the most fundamental material, and of nearly complete flexibility in choice of topics to be covered. Individually the volumes of the Foundations of Modern Organic Chemistry provide introductions in depth to basic areas of organic chemistry; together they comprise a contemporary survey of organic chemistry at an undergraduate level.

KENNETH L. RINEHART, JR.
University of Illinois

Preface

This text is meant to introduce free radical chemistry to the undergraduate. Since undergraduate textbooks in organic chemistry often include very little radical chemistry, it is hoped that this book will encourage the introduction of a more complete coverage of this important area.

Radical chemistry is a newer branch of organic chemistry than the more familiar field of ionic organic reactions. In fact, as W. A. Waters and F. A. Mayo remark, "It was not until . . . 1929 that any serious consideration was given to the conception that radicals played any significant role in simple organic reactions." (*Vistas in Free Radical Chemistry,* New York: Pergamon Press, 1959). Today, however, radical chemistry has achieved tremendous industrial and theoretical importance. Radicals are involved in many of the reactions initiated by light, including photosynthesis, and in combustions, respiration, and many other vital reactions. Many of the processes in which the common plastics, fibers, and rubbers are manufactured involve radical intermediates.

This book can only provide an introduction to the area of free radical chemistry, but it is hoped that the student will wish to read further. References are cited in the text when elementary treatments of the subject are available. Extensive discussion of the reactions mentioned in this book can most conveniently be found by referring to

Radical Reactions
by W. A. Pryor (New York: McGraw-Hill Book Company, 1966)

since these two books are organized in a similar way. The longer book is at an advanced level and includes more quantitative data, a more complete review of the field, more difficult problems, and a considerable number of citations of the original literature.

William A. Pryor

Contents

1

INTRODUCTION 1

1.1 Definitions **1**
1.2 Main Types of Radical Reactions **1**
1.3 Chain Processes and Various Types of Propagation Reactions **2**
1.4 Detection of Free Radicals **5**
1.5 Spectra **6**
1.6 Trapping **7**
1.7 Rates **8**
1.8 Bond Dissociation Energies **9**
1.9 Heats of Formation **10**
Problems **11**
Suggested Further Readings **12**

2

CONFORMATION OF RADICALS 13

2.1 General **13**
2.2 Optically Active Starting Materials **14**
2.3 Rates of Radical Production **16**
Problems **18**

3

THERMAL HOMOLYSIS 19

3.1 Peroxides: Introduction 19
3.2 Dialkyl Peroxides 21
3.3 Acetyl Peroxide 23
3.4 Benzoyl Peroxide 24
3.5 Peresters 25
3.6 Azo Compounds 27
3.7 Hydrogen Peroxide and Organic Hydroperoxides 30
3.8 Molecule-Induced Homolysis 31
Problems 35

4

PHOTOCHEMICAL PRODUCTION OF RADICALS 37

4.1 Introduction 37
4.2 Possible Reactions of Photoexcited Species 37
4.3 Physical Deexcitation Processes 38
4.4 Chemical Deexcitation Processes 40
4.5 Carbonyl Compounds 41
4.6 Energy Transfer 43
Problems 44
Suggested Further Readings 45

5

RADICAL-FORMING REDOX REACTIONS 46

5.1 General 46
5.2 Copper-Catalyzed Reactions 48
Problem 50

6

HYDROGEN ABSTRACTION REACTIONS 51

6.1 General Features of Hydrogen Abstractions 51
6.2 Relative Rates 54
6.3 Polar Effects 56
6.4 Solvent Effects 58
Problems 59
Suggested Further Readings 60

7

HALOGENATION 61

7.1 Fluorination 61
7.2 Chlorination 62
7.3 Bromination 65
7.4 Iodination 65
7.5 Halogenation by Hypohalites 66
7.6 Halogenation by N-Baromosuccinimide 67
Problems 69

8

ADDITION 70

8.1 The Generalized Mechanism of the Reaction 70
8.2 Addition of the Hydrogen Halides and the Halogens 73
8.3 Addition of the Halomethanes 78
8.4 Addition of Thiols and Hydrogen Sulfide 79
Problems 80

9

RADICAL POLYMERIZATIONS 82

9.1 Examples of Useful Polymers 82
9.2 Kinetics of Polymerizations 86
9.3 Copolymerization 89
Problems 90
Suggested Further Readings 91

10

AROMATIC SUBSTITUTION 92

10.1 Phenylation 92
10.2 Benzoyl Peroxide 94
10.3 Reaction of Substituted Phenyl Radicals 96
Problems 97

11

RADICAL REARRANGEMENTS 98

11.1 1,2-Aryl Migrations 98
11.2 1,2-Alkyl and Hydrogen Migrations 101
11.3 1,2-Halogen Migrations 101
11.4 Ring-Opening and Ring-Closing Reactions 101
11.5 1,4- and 1,5-Hydrogen Migrations 103
Problems 104

12

TERMINATION REACTIONS 105

12.1 Introduction **105**
12.2 Third Body Effect **106**
12.3 Combination-Disproportionation Ratios **106**
Problem **107**

INDEX 109

1
Introduction

1.1 DEFINITIONS

In this chapter we shall introduce and define many of the terms used throughout this text. Some of this material will already be familiar to many readers and can be skipped over rapidly,† while certain topics have special significance in a study of radical reactions and may need to be briefly reviewed.

A free radical can be defined as any species having an odd number of electrons. A few examples of species which fit this definition are given in Table 1-1.

Virtually all chemical bonds are made up of two electrons, and bonds therefore can break in two different ways. In the first, both electrons in the bond remain attached to one of the fragments:

$$A—B \longrightarrow A^+ + :B^-$$

Since the two fragments are differently charged, this process is called heterolysis, and the charged fragments are, of course, called ions.

In the second bond-breaking process, the two electrons in the bond divide symmetrically:

$$A—B \longrightarrow A\cdot + B\cdot$$

This process is called homolysis, and the fragments are radicals.

Table 1-1

EXAMPLES OF FREE RADICALS

Species	Names
$CH_3\cdot$	Methyl radical‡
$C_6H_5\cdot$	Phenyl radical
$CH_3—C(=O)—O\cdot$	Acetate radical
$Na\cdot$	Sodium atom
$Cl\cdot$	Chlorine atom or radical§
$NO_2\cdot$	Nitrogen dioxide
$C_6H_6\dot{^-}$	Benzene radical anion
$[H_3C\cdot H]^+$	Methane radical cation§

‡ The names methyl free radical, methyl radical, or simply methyl can be used interchangeably.

§ Note that the pairs of valence electrons are omitted and that only the odd electron is shown.

1.2 MAIN TYPES OF RADICAL REACTIONS

Radical reactions may be divided into three main types: those in which radicals are formed, those in which the site of the odd electron changes, and those in which radicals are destroyed.

† These topics are covered in the volumes in this series by N. L. Allinger and J. Allinger, *Structures of Organic Molecules* (Englewood Cliffs, N.J.: Prentice-Hall, Inc., 1965), and by R. Stewart, *The Investigation of Organic Reactions* (1966).

Radical-forming processes and radical-destroying processes are conceptually quite simple. Radicals are formed in pairs by the cleavage of two-electron bonds. Examples include the thermal or photochemical dissociations of peroxides or halogens,

$$\text{ROOR} \xrightarrow[\text{light}]{\text{heat or}} 2\text{RO}\cdot$$

$$\text{Cl}_2 \xrightarrow[\text{light}]{\text{heat or}} 2\text{Cl}\cdot$$

or of azo compounds:

$$\text{CH}_3\text{—N=N—CH}_3 \xrightarrow[\text{light}]{\text{heat or}} 2\text{CH}_3\cdot + \text{N}_2$$

Radicals are also destroyed in pairs. In the case of atoms, termination occurs by combination processes. For example, one termination reaction is

$$2\text{Cl}\cdot \longrightarrow \text{Cl}_2$$

Methyl radicals also terminate by combination, in this case to form ethane:

$$2\text{CH}_3\cdot \longrightarrow \text{CH}_3\text{—CH}_3$$

More complex alkyl radicals terminate by either combination or disproportionation. The ethyl radical, for example, terminates as shown below:

$$2\text{CH}_3\text{—CH}_2\cdot \xrightarrow{\text{combination}} \text{CH}_3\text{—CH}_2\text{—CH}_2\text{—CH}_3$$

$$2\text{CH}_3\text{—CH}_2\cdot \xrightarrow[\text{tionation}]{\text{dispropor-}} \text{CH}_3\text{—CH}_3 + \text{CH}_2\text{=CH}_2$$

Among the most interesting reactions of radicals are those in which the site of the odd electron changes but the number of radicals does not. Common examples of these reactions are atom-transfer processes; usually a hydrogen or a halogen atom is transferred as illustrated below:

$$\text{R}\cdot + \text{R'H} \longrightarrow \text{RH} + \text{R'}\cdot$$

$$\text{R}\cdot + \text{R'Cl} \longrightarrow \text{RCl} + \text{R'}\cdot$$

$$\text{CH}_3\cdot + \text{CCl}_4 \longrightarrow \text{CH}_3\text{Cl} + \cdot\text{CCl}_3$$

$$\phi\cdot + \text{CCl}_3\text{Br} \longrightarrow \phi\text{Br} + \cdot\text{CCl}_3$$

Reactions such as these are often called *transfer reactions,* and the molecule which reacts with the radical is called the *transfer agent.*

1.3 CHAIN PROCESSES AND VARIOUS TYPES OF PROPAGATION REACTIONS

Radical reactions usually involve chains: an initiation step forms radicals, propagation steps occur in which the number of radicals does not change, and finally termination reactions destroy the radicals and end the chain. An example of a chain process is the light-initiated chlorination of a hydrocarbon, RH:

Initiation:

$$Cl_2 \xrightarrow{\text{light}} 2Cl\cdot$$

Propagation:

$$Cl\cdot + RH \longrightarrow R\cdot + HCl \qquad (1\text{-}1)$$

$$R\cdot + Cl_2 \longrightarrow R{-}Cl + Cl\cdot \qquad (1\text{-}2)$$

Termination:

$$2Cl\cdot \longrightarrow Cl_2$$

$$2R\cdot \longrightarrow R{-}R$$

$$Cl\cdot + R\cdot \longrightarrow R{-}Cl$$

Chlorine molecules absorb light and become sufficiently activated to break the Cl—Cl bond. The chain is propagated by a combination of two steps: Reaction (1-1) is a hydrogen atom transfer that produces the alkyl radical, and Reaction (1-2) is a chlorine atom transfer. Note that the *sum* of Reactions (1-1) and (1-2) is

$$R{-}H + Cl_2 \longrightarrow R{-}Cl + HCl \qquad (1\text{-}3)$$

In the above chlorination, the product alkyl chloride is formed in the propagation reactions. The propagation steps in chain reactions are of great interest, since they are very often the key to understanding the nature of the products which are formed. Reactions which occur as part of the propagation sequence in radical chain reactions are of four main types: 1. atom-transfer reactions, 2. addition reactions, 3. fragmentation reactions, and 4. rearrangements.

1. Atom-transfer Reactions: One or more atom-transfer reactions often occur as propagation steps in chain sequences. As discussed above, these reactions usually involve hydrogen or halogen transfer; a few more examples are:

$$Cl\cdot + \phi CH_3 \longrightarrow HCl + \phi CH_2$$

$$R\cdot + HBr \longrightarrow RH + Br\cdot$$

$$R\cdot + CH_3I \longrightarrow RI + \cdot CH_3$$

2. Addition Reactions: These include the addition of radicals to ordinary olefins; for example,

$$RCH{=}CH_2 + Cl\cdot \longrightarrow R\dot{C}H{-}CH_2Cl$$

$$RCH{=}CH_2 + CH_3\cdot \longrightarrow R\dot{C}H{-}CH_2{-}CH_3$$

Addition occurs so as to form the more stable radical; in the above examples, a secondary radical is formed in preference to a primary radical. For aliphatic radicals, stability increases in the sequence primary < secondary < tertiary.

The radical polymerization of olefins involves an addition reaction as the key step in chain propagation. In this case, a polymeric radical containing n units adds one more unit of the olefin to form the $n + 1$ radical. This can be symbolized† as shown below for the olefin $CH_2{=}CHR$:

$$R'{-}(CH_2{-}\overset{\displaystyle R}{\overset{|}{C}}H)_n\cdot + CH_2{=}CHR \longrightarrow R'{-}(CH_2{-}\overset{\displaystyle R}{\overset{|}{C}}H)_n{-}CH_2{-}\overset{\displaystyle R}{\overset{|}{C}}H\cdot$$

Here also, note that the direction of addition is such as to form the more stable secondary radical rather than the less stable primary radical. This reaction can be abbreviated as

$$M_n\cdot + M \longrightarrow M_{n+1}\cdot$$

where M is a molecule of the polymerizable olefin (called the monomer) and $M_n\cdot$ is a polymeric chain which contains n monomer units.

3. Fragmentation Reactions: Occasionally one of the radicals in the chain undergoes fragmentation. The most common fragmentation reaction is a β-scission, in which a pair of electrons β to the odd electron divides, and a radical fragment is ejected:

$$-\overset{\displaystyle R}{\overset{|}{\underset{|}{C}}}-\dot{\underset{|}{C}}- \longrightarrow R\cdot + \rangle C{=}C\langle$$

This reaction is the reverse of an addition reaction. There are three possible electron pairs which could take part in the β-scission, and it is found experimentally that the β-scission predominates which gives rise to the most stable radical. For example, the alkoxy radical shown below can undergo three different β-scissions which would give three different sets of products:

$$\text{(alkoxy radical)}\text{–O}\cdot \longrightarrow \text{(ketone)} + \cdot CH_3 \quad < 0.5\%$$

$$\longrightarrow \text{(ketone)} + \cdot C_2H_5 \quad 3\%$$

$$\longrightarrow \text{(ketone)} + CH_3{-}\dot{C}H{-}CH_3 \quad 95\%$$

† The nature of the end group R′ need not be considered at this point. We will return to this topic in Chap. 9.

As shown, the products are produced in amounts which parallel the stability of the radicals which are formed: $i\text{-Pr}\cdot > \text{Et}\cdot > \text{Me}\cdot$.

4. Rearrangement: Radical rearrangements are not common, but occasionally the propagation sequence includes a rearrangement. For example, a halogen atom may move as in the reaction of 1-chloropropane with chlorine atoms from HCl:

$$Cl\cdot + CH_3\text{—}\underset{H}{\overset{H}{\underset{|}{\overset{|}{C}}}}\text{—}CH_2Cl \longrightarrow CH_3\text{—}\underset{H}{\underset{|}{\dot{C}}}\text{—}CH_2Cl + HCl$$

$$CH_3\text{—}\underset{H}{\underset{|}{\dot{C}}}\text{—}CH_2Cl \xrightleftharpoons{\text{rearrangement}} CH_3\text{—}\underset{H}{\overset{Cl}{\underset{|}{\overset{|}{C}}}}\text{—}\dot{C}H_2$$

$$CH_3\text{—}\underset{H}{\overset{Cl}{\underset{|}{\overset{|}{C}}}}\text{—}CH_2\cdot + HCl \longrightarrow CH_3\text{—}\underset{H}{\overset{Cl}{\underset{|}{\overset{|}{C}}}}\text{—}CH_3 + Cl\cdot$$

1.4 DETECTION OF FREE RADICALS

Most radicals are so reactive that they normally only exist in extremely dilute solutions. However, the presence and nature of even these reactive radicals can frequently be detected by the magnetic properties due to the odd electron.

The earliest method of detecting radical species was by magnetic susceptibility measurements. Most substances are diamagnetic; that is, they exert a force to move out of a magnetic field when they are placed between the poles of a powerful magnet. This force is due to the fact that all of the paired electrons in the molecule align themselves so as to oppose the external magnetic field. Substances with unpaired electrons, however, are paramagnetic and are drawn into a magnetic field. In these substances, the paramagnetic contribution by the odd electron opposes the diamagnetic contribution of all of the paired electrons. The magnetic susceptibility of substances can be measured by the force exerted on them when they are in a magnetic field using a device such as the Gouy balance.

A technique was invented in 1945 which directly measures the paramagnetism of an odd electron. The method is called either electron paramagnetic resonance or electron spin resonance (epr or esr). An electron can be thought of as having spin and an associated magnetic moment. When an external magnetic field is applied, the electron magnetic moment can be oriented either with or against the field, and therefore, the electron can exist in either of two energy levels. Transitions between these two

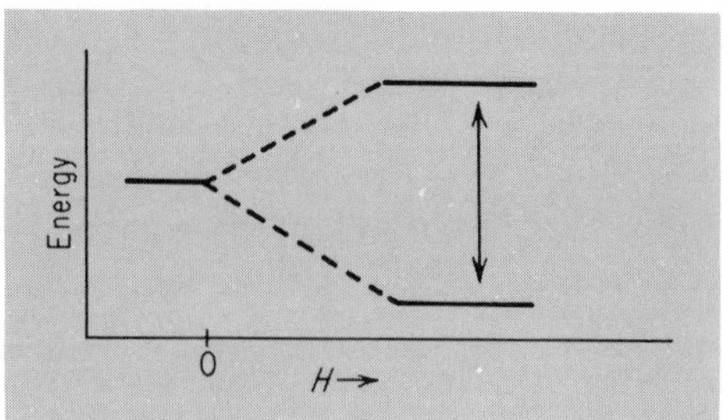

Fig. 1-1 Transition for an electron in a magnetic field *H*.

levels cause an absorption line to appear in the microwave region of the spectrum (Fig. 1-1). Most epr spectra consist of more than one line as a result of what is called hyperfine splitting. If the odd electron in a radical is located on an atom which has a nucleus with a magnetic moment, then the magnetic moment of the nucleus interacts with the electron and splits its energy levels further. Examples of atoms having nuclei with magnetic moments are: H, F^{19}, N^{15}, C^{13}, and P^{31}.

Consider the case in which an odd electron interacts with one proton. The magnetic field of the proton produces a small additional field which adds to or subtracts from the external magnetic field. Each level in Fig. 1-1 is then split in two by interaction with a proton (Fig. 1-2). Nuclear spins do not change when the electron changes levels, and therefore, transitions are observed between half of the levels in Fig. 1-2; i.e., those which have the same nuclear spin. Thus, two transitions occur, and the electron which produced a single epr line now produces a pair of lines. Examples of radicals which would be predicted to give a two line spectrum are H· and $\cdot CHCl_2$. When *n* equivalent protons interact with the electron, the spectrum consists of $n + 1$ lines. For example, the methyl radical with three protons should give a spectrum of four lines. Figure 1-3 shows the spectra of H· and $\cdot CH_3$, which contain two and four lines as predicted. Note that the amount of splitting is greater for H· than for $\cdot CH_3$. In the hydrogen atom, the electron is actually on the atom with a nuclear spin; in the methyl radical, the electron is on the carbon atom and a lesser interaction is observed with the adjacent hydrogen atoms.

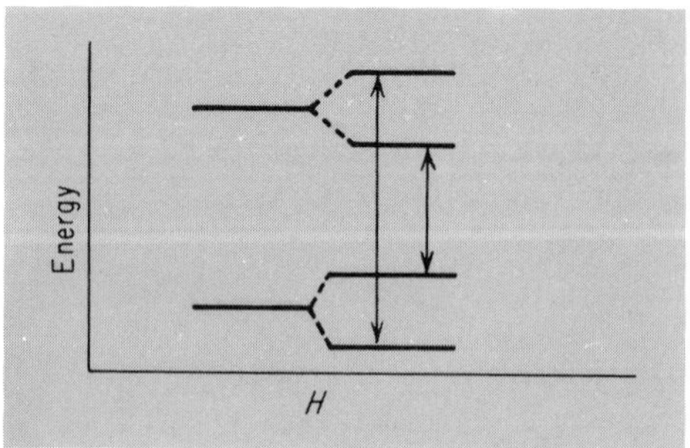

Fig. 1-2 Transitions for an electron interacting with one proton in a magnetic field *H*.

1.5 SPECTRA

In many cases, optical spectra can be used to identify free radicals. The triphenylmethyl radical is yellow in solution:

$$\phi_3C{-}C\phi_3 \rightleftharpoons 2\phi_3C\cdot$$

colorless and diamagnetic — yellow and paramagnetic

If iodine or oxygen is present, the yellow color fades.

$$\phi_3C\cdot + O_2 \longrightarrow \underset{\text{colorless}}{\phi_3C{-}O{-}O\cdot}$$

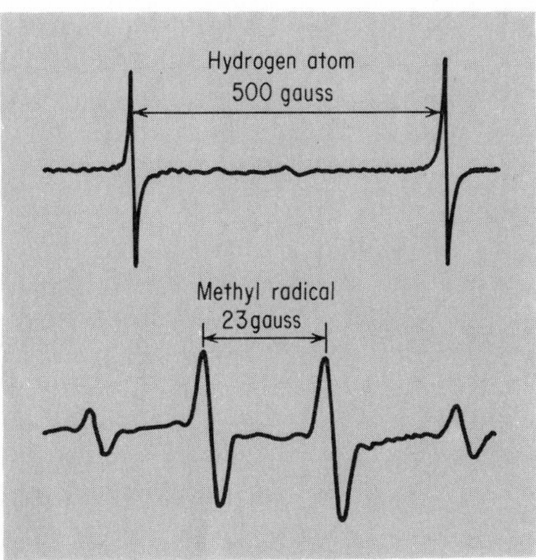

Fig. 1-3 The epr spectra of the hydrogen atom and the methyl radical. (*Varian Associates.*)

The triphenylmethyl radical is unusually stable both because of the bulky phenyl groups around each carbon which hinder coupling, and also because of the large number of resonance structures which delocalize the odd electron density into the rings. It will be helpful at this point to examine these resonance structures since they involve movement of electrons in a homolytic fashion rather than as electron pairs. For example, the odd electron density can be placed at the *ortho* position in one ring as shown below:

$\phi_2C\cdot$ ⟷ ϕ_2C

Diphenylpicrylhydrazine can be oxidized to the hydrazyl radical:

$$\phi_2N{-}N(H){-}C_6H_2(NO_2)_3 \xrightarrow[\text{oxidation}]{PbO_2} \phi_2N{-}\dot{N}{-}C_6H_2(NO_2)_3$$

diphenylpicrylhydrazine → diphenylpicrylhydrazyl (DPPH)

The DPPH radical is deep violet and stable in the solid form for years. Even 10^{-5} *M* solutions of it are measurably colored, and it can be used as an "indicator" to detect the presence of radicals much as an acid-base indicator might be used in a titration.

1.6 TRAPPING

If species which are known to react rapidly with radicals affect the rate of a reaction, it can be concluded that radicals are involved. For example, DPPH inhibits polymerization of monomeric olefins such as styrene. The conclusion is that the polymerization involves radical intermediates, and that these intermediates are trapped by the DPPH. In solution, iodine, quinones, oxygen, sulfur, and many other substances have been used as radical scavengers. In the gas phase, butadiene has been used; the radicals add to the diene to produce a product which dimerizes, and the dimer can be isolated and identified.

1.7 RATES

Radicals usually react with other materials very rapidly. The rate at which radicals disappear depends both on the inherent stability (or, conversely, the reactivity) of the radicals and their concentration, and also on the reactivity and concentration of the other substances present.

It will be helpful at this point to review briefly the expression for reaction rates.† The rate of the reaction

$$a\mathrm{A} \longrightarrow b\mathrm{B}$$

is given by

$$\text{rate} = \frac{1}{a}\frac{-d(\mathrm{A})}{dt} = \frac{1}{b}\frac{+d(\mathrm{B})}{dt} = k(\mathrm{A})^n$$

where the parentheses indicate concentrations (moles/liter for work in solution) and the fractions $1/a$ and $1/b$ are statistical corrections based on the stoichiometry of the reaction. The reaction rate depends on the concentration of A raised to the nth power and is said to be of the order n.

The amount of energy which a molecule must possess in order to react is called the activation energy, E. Figure 1-4 shows this energy, and also shows the activation energy necessary for the reverse reaction, E'. Note that the heat of reaction, ΔH, is equal to the difference between the two activation energies:

$$\Delta H = E - E' \qquad (1\text{-}4)$$

(The energy levels shown in Fig. 1-4 are above the energy minima due to the zero point energy of vibration.)

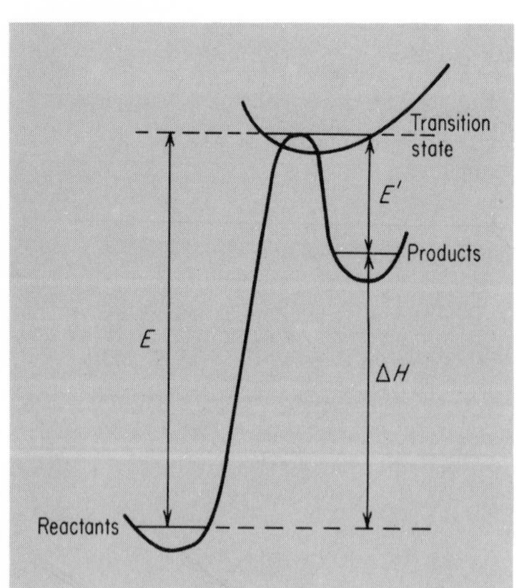

Fig. 1-4 Activation energy and heat of reaction.

† The use of kinetics in organic reactions is covered in the text in this series by R. Stewart, *The Investigation of Organic Reactions* (Englewood Cliffs, N.J.: Prentice-Hall, Inc., 1966).

The knowledge of activation energies is of great importance in understanding the driving forces behind chemical reactions. Quantities that approximate the activation energy can be obtained by studying the variation of reaction rate with temperature. The most commonly used equation which expresses this variation is the Arrhenius equation:

$$k = Ae^{-E_a/RT} \tag{1-5}$$

Most reactions are found to obey this equation; that is, the rate constant can be expressed in terms of two parameters, an Arrhenius activation energy E_a and a pre-exponential term A which is related to the probability of the reaction occurring at any given temperature. Note that low values of E_a and large values of A imply fast reaction rates. Experimental values of E_a are excellent approximations for the theoretical activation energy E shown in Fig. 1-4. A textbook on physical chemistry should be consulted for the methods of calculating E_a and A from kinetic data.

1.8 BOND DISSOCIATION ENERGIES

There are several methods for obtaining bond energies, and an elementary text on physical chemistry should be consulted for details. One method, however, will be mentioned here. In the reaction

$$\text{AB} \longrightarrow \text{A}\cdot + \text{B}\cdot$$

the bond dissociation energy $D(\text{A—B})$ is equal to the heat of reaction:

$$D(\text{A—B}) = \Delta H$$

If the activation energy for the reverse reaction (i.e., the recombination of the radicals) is zero, and if the radicals are formed in their ground states, then from Equation (1-4):

$$E_a = \Delta H$$

and

$$D(\text{A—B}) = E_a = \Delta H \tag{1-6}$$

Thus the bond dissociation energy of the A—B bond can be obtained from the Arrhenius activation energy for dissociation of AB.

As an example of this method, consider the dissociation of *t*-butyl peroxide:

$$t\text{-BuO—OBu-}t \longrightarrow t\text{-BuO}\cdot + \cdot\text{OBu-}t$$

The bond dissociation energy of the O—O bond, $D(t\text{-BuO—OBu-}t)$, is calculated to be 37 kcal/mole from the activation energy for the dissociation of the peroxide obtained from kinetic studies. As we shall see in the next section, dissociation energies can be used to predict the heat of reaction.

1.9 HEATS OF FORMATION

Heats of formation can be calculated from bond energy data, and a knowledge of some heats of formation allows prediction of the energetics of other reactions. The heat of formation ΔH_f° is defined as the energy change when a substance is formed from the elements in their normal states at 25°C and 1 atm. As an example of the calculation of heats of formation, consider the calculation of the heat of formation of the hydrogen atom from the dissociation of hydrogen gas:

$$H_2 \longrightarrow 2H\cdot \qquad \Delta H = 103.4 \text{ kcal/mole}$$

The heat of reaction is equal to the sum of the heats of formation of all of the products minus the sum of the heats of formation of all of the reactants:

$$\Delta H = \Sigma\, \Delta H_f^\circ \text{ (products)} - \Sigma\, \Delta H_f^\circ \text{ (reactants)}$$

Therefore, for hydrogen,

$$\Delta H = 103.4 = 2\Delta H_f^\circ(\text{H}\cdot) - \Delta H_f^\circ(\text{H}_2)$$

$$\Delta H_f^\circ(\text{H}\cdot) = \frac{103.4 + 0}{2} = 52 \text{ kcal/mole}$$

Notice that the heat of formation of elemental hydrogen is zero by definition.

Next, consider the calculation of the heat of formation of a *t*-butoxy radical. The heat of formation of *t*-butyl alcohol can be calculated to be −77 kcal/mole from its measured heat of combustion. The bond dissociation energy of the O—H bond has been measured by various methods and is found to be about 104 kcal/mole. Therefore, for the reaction

$$t\text{-BuO—H} \longrightarrow t\text{-BuO}\cdot + \text{H}\cdot$$

we can write

$$\Delta H_f^\circ(\text{H}\cdot) + \Delta H_f^\circ(t\text{-BuO}\cdot) - \Delta H_f^\circ(t\text{-BuOH}) = 104 \text{ kcal/mole}$$

and solving for the heat of formation of the *t*-butoxy radical gives

$$\Delta H_f^\circ(t\text{-BuO}\cdot) = 104 - 52 + (-77) = -25 \text{ kcal/mole}$$

The heat of formation of the *t*-butoxy radical which we have just calculated can be used to predict the activation energy for the reaction

$$t\text{-BuO—OBu-}t \longrightarrow 2t\text{-BuO}\cdot$$

The heat of formation for *t*-butyl peroxide (TBP) can be calculated from its measured heat of combustion, and it is found to be −85 kcal/mole. Therefore, the activation energy for the dissociation of the peroxide, which should be equal to the bond energy of the O—O bond, is:

$$\Delta H = E_a = 2\Delta H_f^\circ(t\text{-BuO}\cdot) - \Delta H_f^\circ(\text{TBP})$$
$$= 2(-25) - (-85) = 35 \text{ kcal/mole}$$

Notice that this prediction is within 2 kcal/mole of the activation energy obtained experimentally. (See p. 9.)

The heat of reaction can be calculated from a knowledge of bond dissociation energies. For example, consider the reactions:

	Reaction	Heat of reaction
	A—B ⟶ A· + B·	ΔH_1
	B—C ⟶ B· + C·	ΔH_2
Difference:	A—B + C· ⟶ B—C + A·	$\Delta H_1 - \Delta H_2 = \Delta H_3$

Now, if the assumptions necessary for Equation (1-6) to apply are met:

$$\Delta H_1 = D(\text{A—B})$$
$$\Delta H_2 = D(\text{B—C})$$

and, therefore,

$$\Delta H_3 = \Delta H_1 - \Delta H_2 = D(\text{A—B}) - D(\text{B—C}) \tag{1-7}$$

Thus, the heat of reaction is simply the difference in the bond dissociation energies of the bonds which are broken and those which are formed. For example, the heat of reaction of chlorine atoms with methane can be calculated as

$$CH_4 + Cl\cdot \longrightarrow HCl + \cdot CH_3$$
$$\Delta H = D(CH_3\text{—H}) - D(\text{H—Cl}) = 101 - 102 = -1 \text{ kcal/mole}$$

The reaction is about 1 kcal/mole exothermic since a slightly stronger bond is formed than is broken.

PROBLEMS

1. Give the three main types of radical processes and exemplify each.

2. Give four types of propagation reactions and exemplify.

3. Write resonance structures for the triphenylmethyl radical. How many resonance structures should exist? Why does the color of the triphenylmethyl radical fade in the presence of air?

4. Write the product of the reaction of methyl radicals with butadiene. Why is the reaction product more stable than the methyl radical?

5. Draw a figure analogous to Fig. 1-4 for an exothermic reaction, and derive an equation like Equation (1-4) for this case. Explain the significance of the difference in the two figures.

6. Given $D(\text{H—Br}) = 87$, $D(\text{RS—H}) = 89$, $D(\phi\text{CH}_2\text{—H}) = 77$, and $D(\text{CH}_3\text{—H}) = 102$ kcal/mole, plus the other dissociation energies given in the text, calculate the heat of reaction for these processes:

$$t\text{-BuO}\cdot + \phi\text{CH}_3 \longrightarrow t\text{-BuOH} + \phi\dot{\text{C}}\text{H}_2$$

$$\text{Br}\cdot + \text{CH}_4 \longrightarrow \text{HBr} + \cdot\text{CH}_3$$

$$\text{CH}_3\cdot + \text{RSH} \longrightarrow \text{CH}_4 + \text{RS}\cdot$$

$$\text{CH}_3\cdot + t\text{-BuOH} \longrightarrow \text{CH}_4 + t\text{-BuO}\cdot$$

7. The pre-exponential term A for a unimolecular reaction is frequently found to be about 10^{12} sec^{-1}. Using 37 kcal/mole for the dissociation energy of t-butyl peroxide, calculate the rate constant for its dissociation at 60° and 150°C. Calculate its half-life (time for half the material to decompose) at these two temperatures.

SUGGESTED FURTHER READINGS

The student may wish to read further or review the following topics: thermodynamic calculations; kinetics and reaction rates; and bond energies. Any of the textbooks on physical chemistry may be consulted, but the following specific reference may be helpful:

Moore, W. J., *Physical Chemistry* (3rd ed.). Englewood Cliffs, N.J.: Prentice-Hall, Inc., 1963. See p. 50, Heats of Reaction; p. 57, Bond Energies; Chap. 8, Kinetics.

2 Conformation of Radicals

2.1 GENERAL

Before turning to a study of the chemical reactions involved in typical initiation and propagation reactions, it will be helpful to become more familiar with the nature of organic free radicals. In this chapter we shall consider the question of the geometry about a carbon atom bearing an odd electron. There are three possibilities: the carbon could be tetrahedral, or planar, or a shallow pyramid which is neither planar nor tetrahedral. Figure 2-1 shows these three possible conformations. Although this is a subject which is still under investigation, it now appears likely that most radicals are either planar or are very slightly pyramidal.

If the radical were planar, then the hybridization of the bonds would be sp^2, just as in a carbonium ion, and the remaining orbital would contain the odd electron (Fig. 2-1a). If the radical were pyramidal, then the orbital containing the electron would be some hybrid between sp^2 and sp^3 and there would be a dissymmetric distribution of electron density in any one conformation of the radical. Figure 2-2 shows the two enantiomorphic conformations of a pyramidal radical.

It would seem that the geometry of radicals might be most suitably probed by physical techniques, but so far these have not provided definitive answers for complex organic radicals. However, physical data are available for the methyl radical; its ultraviolet spectrum implies that it has a ground state which is either planar or does not deviate by more than

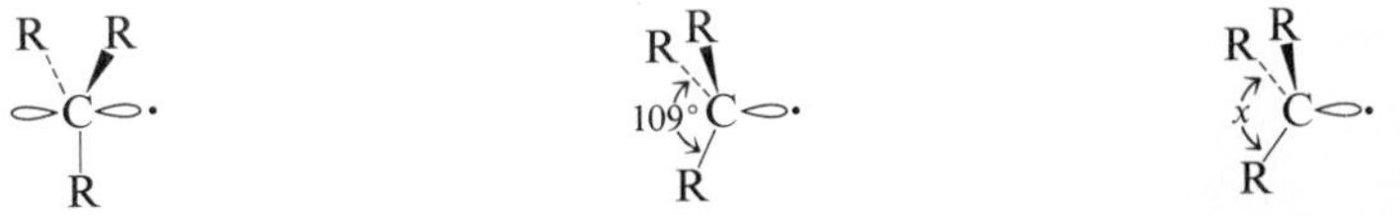

(a) planar radical (sp^2) (b) tetrahedral radical (sp^3) (c) pyramidal radical

Fig. 2-1 The three possible conformations of the radical $R_3C\cdot$.

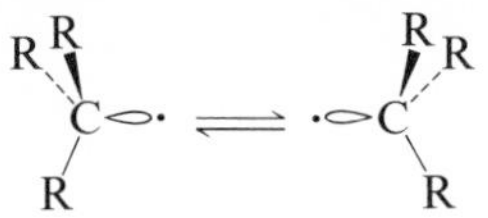

$$R_3C\cdot \rightleftharpoons \cdot CR_3$$

Fig. 2-2 Inversion of a pyramidal radical.

about 15° from planarity. Its epr spectrum is consistent with this, and shows that the energy barrier between a planar structure and a shallow pyramid is very low.

2.2 OPTICALLY ACTIVE STARTING MATERIALS

If radicals were planar, they would have a plane of symmetry and could not exist in optically active forms. Therefore, one approach that has been used to determine whether or not radicals are planar has been to prepare them from optically active starting materials. A number of such experiments have been done, but none has provided an unambiguous answer to the general question: Is it possible to convert an asymmetric carbon atom to a free radical and then back to a stable molecule *without racemization?* For example, the chlorination of optically active 1-chloro-2-methylbutane gives reaction products which do not retain any of the optical activity:

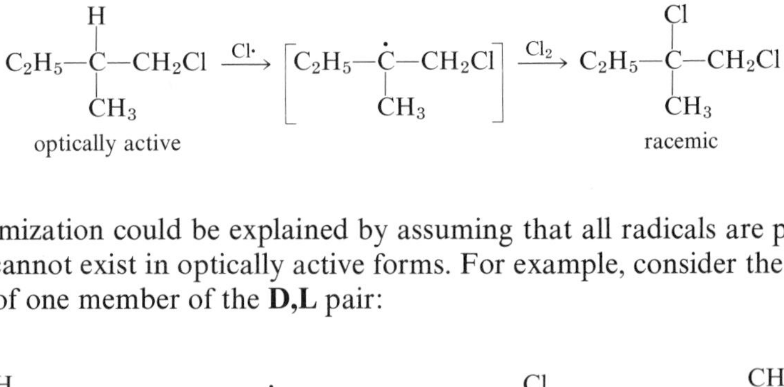

$$\underset{\text{optically active}}{C_2H_5\text{—}CH(CH_3)\text{—}CH_2Cl} \xrightarrow{Cl\cdot} \left[C_2H_5\text{—}\dot{C}(CH_3)\text{—}CH_2Cl\right] \xrightarrow{Cl_2} \underset{\text{racemic}}{C_2H_5\text{—}CCl(CH_3)\text{—}CH_2Cl}$$

Racemization could be explained by assuming that all radicals are planar and cannot exist in optically active forms. For example, consider the reaction of one member of the **D,L** pair:

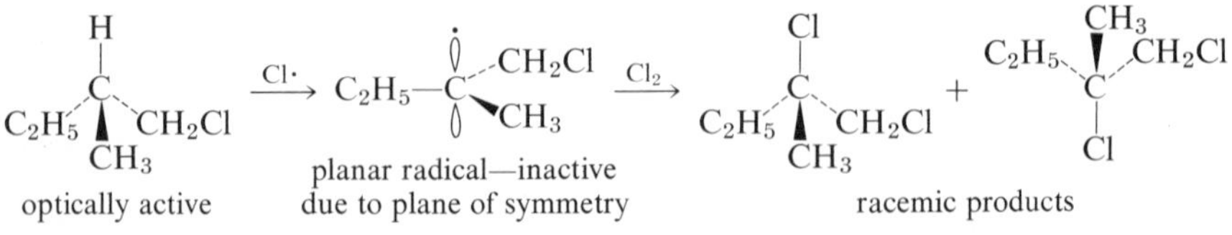

$$\underset{\text{optically active}}{HC(C_2H_5)(CH_2Cl)(CH_3)} \xrightarrow{Cl\cdot} \underset{\substack{\text{planar radical—inactive}\\ \text{due to plane of symmetry}}}{C_2H_5\text{—}\dot{C}(CH_2Cl)(CH_3)} \xrightarrow{Cl_2} \underset{\text{racemic products}}{ClC(C_2H_5)(CH_2Cl)(CH_3) + CH_3C(C_2H_5)(CH_2Cl)Cl}$$

Alternatively, the radicals could be assumed to be pyramidal but to invert faster than they react with chlorine. For example,

$$\text{C}_2\text{H}_5\text{C(H)(CH}_3\text{)CH}_2\text{Cl} \xrightarrow{\text{Cl}\cdot} \text{C}_2\text{H}_5\dot{\text{C}}\text{(CH}_3\text{)CH}_2\text{Cl} \underset{\text{bration of pyramidal radicals}}{\overset{\text{rapid equili-}}{\rightleftharpoons}} \text{C}_2\text{H}_5\dot{\text{C}}\text{(CH}_3\text{)CH}_2\text{Cl}$$

$$\xrightarrow[\text{slower}]{\text{Cl}_2} \text{C}_2\text{H}_5\text{C(Cl)(CH}_3\text{)CH}_2\text{Cl} + \text{C}_2\text{H}_5\text{C(Cl)(CH}_3\text{)CH}_2\text{Cl}$$

racemic products

If radicals are in fact pyramidal, then a faster transfer agent than chlorine might be able to scavenge the first-formed radicals before they can invert. Bromine is known to be a better transfer agent than chlorine, and bromination of optically active starting materials does sometimes lead to optically active products. For example, bromination of either optically active 1-chloro- or 1-bromo-2-methylbutane gives some retention of optical activity in the products. In terms of our discussion above, we can explain this by postulating that bromine molecules react with radicals so rapidly that they trap the optically active radicals before they can racemize by inversion. For example, the **D** molecules can be envisioned reacting as below:

$$\underset{\textbf{D}\ (\text{X} = \text{Cl or Br})}{\text{C}_2\text{H}_5\text{—C(H)(CH}_3\text{)—CH}_2\text{X}} \xrightarrow{\text{Br}\cdot} \underset{\textbf{D}}{\text{C}_2\text{H}_5\text{—}\dot{\text{C}}\text{(CH}_3\text{)—CH}_2\text{X}}$$

$$\underset{\textbf{D}}{\text{C}_2\text{H}_5\text{—}\dot{\text{C}}\text{(CH}_3\text{)—CH}_2\text{X}} \xrightarrow[\text{very fast}]{\text{Br}_2} \underset{\textbf{D}}{\text{C}_2\text{H}_5\text{—C(Br)(CH}_3\text{)—CH}_2\text{X}}$$

$$\underset{\textbf{D}}{\text{C}_2\text{H}_5\text{—}\dot{\text{C}}\text{(CH}_3\text{)—CH}_2\text{X}} \overset{\text{slower}}{\rightleftharpoons} \underset{\textbf{L}}{\text{C}_2\text{H}_5\text{—}\dot{\text{C}}\text{(CH}_3\text{)—CH}_2\text{X}}$$

However, there also is the possibility that optically active products are obtained from these α-halo radicals because the halogen atom is able to bridge and form a triangular radical that cannot invert and racemize. This can be symbolized as below:

$$\underset{\mathbf{D}}{C_2H_5-\overset{H}{\underset{CH_3}{C}}-CH_2X} \xrightarrow{Br\cdot} \underset{\mathbf{D}}{C_2H_5-\overset{X}{\underset{CH_3}{C}}\overset{\cdot}{=\!=}CH_2} \xrightarrow{Br_2} \underset{\mathbf{D}}{C_2H_5-\overset{Br}{\underset{CH_3}{C}}-CH_2X}$$

This possibility cannot be ignored since both chlorine and bromine atoms are known to migrate to adjacent atoms in free radical processes (for example, see page 5), and the transition state for this rearrangement must involve a halogen atom which is partly bonded to each carbon atom. If bridged radicals are formed directly from the starting materials as shown above, then the formation of optically active products in this system in no way indicates the preferred geometry of open-chain radicals.

Since racemization occurs in chlorination, open-chain radicals must exist; the question is whether bridged radicals also exist. If bridged radicals are postulated, the difference between chlorination and bromination can be explained by assuming that bromine scavenges the bridged radicals before they can racemize via their open-chain counterparts. Although bridged radicals are not necessary to explain the results we have discussed here, there is some direct evidence which supports the existance of halogen-bridged radicals in other related systems. We shall return to the question of bridged versus open-chain radicals when we discuss the addition of bromine atoms to olefins in Sec. 8.2 on page 75.

2.3 RATES OF RADICAL PRODUCTION

Evidence about the preferred conformation of radicals can be derived from studies of the rates at which radicals are formed from substances of known geometry. These studies show that radicals are formed at about the same rates in ordinary unstrained systems as they are in systems which are held in either a planar or in a non-planar configuration. Apparently, the difference in energy between a planar radical and a non-planar one is small, and the energetics of radical reactions is not very sensitive to geometry.

Bicyclic compounds cannot become planar at the bridgehead position and for this reason carbonium ions, which prefer to be planar, are formed at bridgehead positions extremely slowly:

$$\text{(bicyclic)}-Cl \xrightarrow{\text{very slow}} \text{(bicyclic)}^{+} + Cl^-$$

highly strained carbonium ion

However, the comparable radical reactions proceed with nearly normal rates. For example, the analogous peroxide, apocamphoyl peroxide, dissociates in carbon tetrachloride to give normal products:

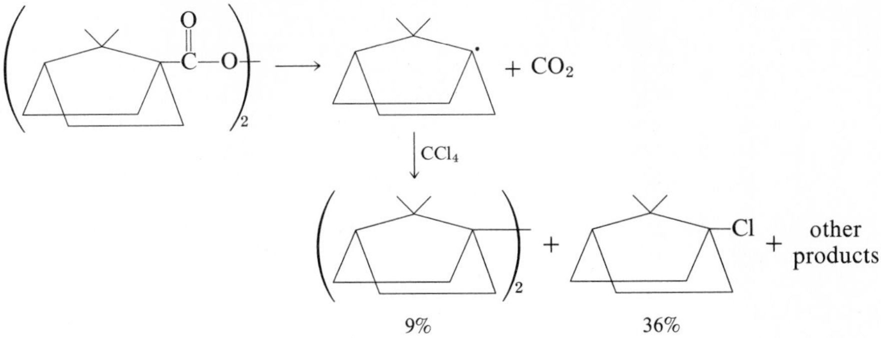

$$\left(\text{bridgehead}-\overset{O}{\overset{\|}{C}}-O-\right)_2 \longrightarrow \text{bridgehead radical} + CO_2$$

$$\downarrow CCl_4$$

$$(\text{bridgehead})_2 \quad 9\% \quad + \quad \text{bridgehead}-Cl \quad 36\% \quad + \text{ other products}$$

It is apparent from the products that the bridgehead radical is formed in this reaction and that it is not of especially high energy.

The triptyl structure offers another example of the same phenomena:

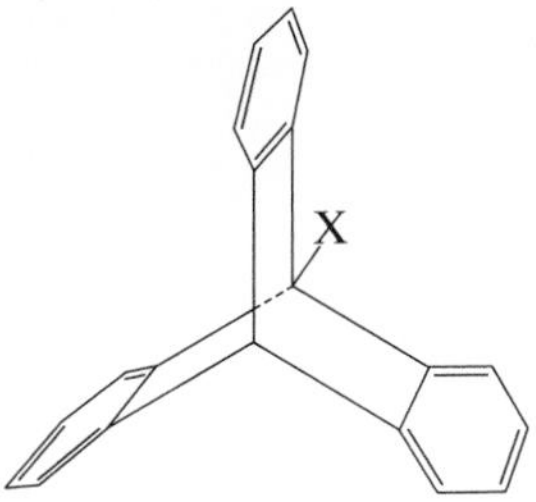

triptyl halide (Tr—X)

Triptyl carbonium ions are formed very slowly since the ion cannot become planar:

$$Tr{-}X \xrightarrow{\text{very slow}} Tr^+ + X^-$$

Triptoyl peroxide, on the other hand, reacts as shown below:

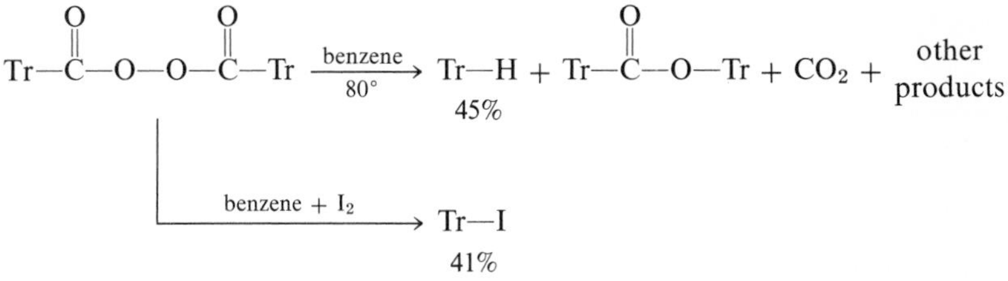

$$Tr{-}\overset{O}{\overset{\|}{C}}{-}O{-}O{-}\overset{O}{\overset{\|}{C}}{-}Tr \xrightarrow[80^\circ]{\text{benzene}} \underset{45\%}{Tr{-}H} + Tr{-}\overset{O}{\overset{\|}{C}}{-}O{-}Tr + CO_2 + \text{other products}$$

$$\xrightarrow{\text{benzene} + I_2} \underset{41\%}{Tr{-}I}$$

The isolation of triptyl iodide in the presence of iodine leaves no doubt that triptyl radicals are involved in these reactions. The fact that the triptyl radical abstracts hydrogen from benzene, which is a very unreactive hydrogen donor, indicates that it is somewhat higher in energy than an ordinary radical.

PROBLEMS

1. Apocamphoyl peroxide dissociates into radicals at a rate very similar to that of benzoyl peroxide (ϕ—CO_2—O_2C—ϕ) at 60°C. Does this fact have any bearing on the geometry of radical centers at carbon atoms? The dissociation of apocamphoyl peroxide in carbon tetrachloride leads to some apocamphyl chloride. Does this fact have a bearing on the geometry of carbon radicals?

2. Discuss the question of whether or not radicals can exist in optically active forms. In your discussion, include these facts: optically active 1-bromo- and 1-chloro-2-methylbutane can be brominated to produce optically active products, but chlorination gives only racemic products; bromination of 1-bromo-2-methylbutane gives only 1,2-dibromo-2-methylbutane, and 1-chloro-2-methylbutane gives only 2-bromo-1-chloro-2-methylbutane; chlorination of either 1-bromo- or 1-chloro-2-methylbutane gives a diverse mixture of racemic products.

3
Thermal Homolysis

Radicals can be produced in three ways: by thermal scission of bonds, by irradiating molecules to break bonds, and by one-electron oxidation-reduction processes. In this chapter we shall discuss the reactions of compounds which readily undergo thermal decomposition and are used as initiators of radical processes. In Chap. 4 we will take up production of radicals by the interaction of light with molecules; in Chap. 5 we will discuss redox reactions.

3.1 PEROXIDES: INTRODUCTION

When molecules are heated to sufficiently high temperatures, bonds break and radicals are formed. The normal carbon-carbon bond energy is about 90 kcal/mole, and thermal excitation of molecules becomes sufficient to break these bonds at temperatures in the range of 450° to 650°C. For example, this is the temperature region in which thermal cracking of petroleum is carried out. However, some compounds that have exceptionally weak bonds decompose to form radicals at lower temperatures, and these compounds can be used to initiate radical reactions at temperatures of 50° to 150°C. The most frequently used compounds of this type are the class of initiators containing the peroxide O—O bond. Table 3-1 lists a number of the commercially available, commonly used peroxides, the Arrhenius activation energy for their decomposition, and the temperature at which they produce radicals with a 1 hr half-life.

Peroxides are subject to decomposition by at least three different homolytic mechanisms. In the first, a *unimolecular scission* of the peroxidic bond occurs:

$$\text{RO—OR} \longrightarrow 2\text{RO}\cdot$$

The radicals produced by this dissociation can either decompose further (for example, by a β-scission) or can attack other molecules present in the system and initiate radical processes.

The second decomposition mechanism of peroxides is a bimolecular process called *induced decomposition.* This process involves radicals attack-

Table 3-1

FREQUENTLY USED PEROXIDE INITIATORS

Name	Structure	Arrhenius activation energy (kcal/mole)	°C for 1 hr half-life
t-Butyl peroxide	*t*-BuO—OBu-*t*	37	150
t-Butyl perbenzoate	*t*-BuO—O—C(=O)—φ	34	125
Benzoyl peroxide	φ—C(=O)—O—O—C(=O)—φ	30†	95†
Acetyl peroxide	CH_3—C(=O)—O—O—C(=O)—CH_3	30†	85†

† Solvent dependent. Data given for inert solvents.

ing the peroxide to cause its decomposition; the attacking radicals can be those from the peroxide itself or they can be secondary radicals from some subsequent reaction. The mechanism of the induced decomposition depends on the structure of the peroxide. For simple alkyl peroxides it is thought to be hydrogen abstraction from the α-carbon atom to produce an intermediate radical which undergoes β-scission:

$$R\cdot + R'_2CH{-}O{-}O{-}CHR'_2 \longrightarrow RH + R'_2\dot{C}{-}O{-}O{-}CHR'_2$$

$$R'_2\dot{C}{-}O{-}O{-}CHR'_2 \longrightarrow R'_2C{=}O + \cdot O{-}CHR'_2$$

For benzoyl peroxide it is an attack on the peroxidic O—O bond:

$$R\cdot + \phi{-}\overset{\overset{\displaystyle O}{\|}}{C}{-}O{-}O{-}\overset{\overset{\displaystyle O}{\|}}{C}{-}\phi \longrightarrow \phi{-}CO_2\cdot + R{-}O{-}\overset{\overset{\displaystyle O}{\|}}{C}{-}\phi$$

When peroxides are used to initiate radical reactions, the occurrence of an induced decomposition reaction wastes some of the initiator since it destroys a molecule of peroxide without increasing the number of radicals.

The third decomposition reaction of peroxides is a little understood *detonation* which makes all peroxidic compounds hazardous to handle. Peroxides differ in their susceptibility to explosion; in general, the lower the molecular weight, the more dangerous the peroxide. Of the alkyl peroxides, methyl peroxide is extremely hazardous, whereas *t*-butyl peroxide is unusually stable and may be distilled at atmospheric pressure. Among acyl peroxides, acetyl peroxide is very hazardous, whereas benzoyl peroxide is much less so. However, any peroxide is potentially dangerous and should not be ground, jarred, or heated under conditions which are not known to be safe.

3.2 DIALKYL PEROXIDES

All of the alkyl peroxides ROOR decompose at similar rates and with activation energies of 34–37 kcal/mole, regardless of the structure of the R groups. However, the ultimate products formed do depend on the structure of the peroxide used. For example, ethyl peroxide decomposes to produce ethanol and acetaldehyde. These products could result from a disproportionation between ethoxy radicals:

$$CH_3{-}CH_2O{-}OCH_2{-}CH_3 \longrightarrow 2CH_3{-}CH_2O\cdot$$

$$2CH_3{-}CH_2O\cdot \longrightarrow CH_3{-}CH_2{-}OH + CH_3{-}CHO$$

They could also result from a chain process in which an ethoxy radical abstracts an α-hydrogen from a peroxide molecule to produce an intermediate radical which subsequently decomposes by β-scission:

$$CH_3CH_2O\cdot + CH_3CH_2O{-}OCH_2CH_3 \longrightarrow CH_3CH_2OH + CH_3\dot{C}H{-}O{-}OCH_2CH_3$$

$$CH_3\dot{C}H{-}O{-}OCH_2CH_3 \longrightarrow CH_3CHO + CH_3CH_2O\cdot$$

Because its stability makes it safe to handle, *t*-butyl peroxide has been studied in more detail than have the other alkyl peroxides. It decomposes at almost the same rate in both concentrated solutions and the dilute gas phase, and so it can be concluded that the majority of the peroxide decomposes by a unimolecular, non-chain path. If an appreciable fraction of the peroxide decomposed in an induced reaction of high chain length, then the rate would be expected to be higher in solution where radical concentrations are higher and where reactions between radicals and the peroxide would be more probable. The mechanism of the decomposition in the dilute gas phase is shown below; the methyl radicals dimerize nearly quantitatively and the main products are acetone and ethane:

$$t\text{-BuO}{-}\text{OBu-}t \longrightarrow 2t\text{-BuO}\cdot \qquad (3\text{-}1)$$

$$(CH_3)_3C{-}O\cdot \xrightarrow{\beta\text{-scission}} CH_3{-}\overset{\displaystyle O}{\overset{\|}{C}}{-}CH_3 + \cdot CH_3 \qquad (3\text{-}2)$$

$$2CH_3\cdot \longrightarrow C_2H_6 \qquad (3\text{-}3)$$

In pure liquid peroxide as solvent, the products are:

$$t\text{-BuO}{-}\text{OBu-}t \longrightarrow \underset{1.0\text{ to }0.7}{\overset{CH_2}{\underset{CH_3}{O{-}C{-}CH_3}}} + \underset{0.50}{t\text{-BuOH}} + \underset{0.66}{CH_3{-}\overset{\displaystyle O}{\overset{\|}{C}}{-}CH_3} + \underset{0.63}{CH_4} + \underset{0.02}{C_2H_6}$$

mole/mole peroxide

Acetone and ethane result from Reactions (3-2) and (3-3); methane arises from hydrogen abstraction from the peroxide by methyl radicals:

$$CH_3\cdot + t\text{-BuO—O—}\underset{CH_3}{\overset{CH_3}{\underset{|}{\overset{|}{C}}}}\text{—}CH_3 \longrightarrow CH_4 + t\text{-BuO—O—}\underset{CH_3}{\overset{\cdot CH_2}{\underset{|}{\overset{|}{C}}}}\text{—}CH_3$$

I

t-Butyl alcohol is formed by a similar hydrogen abstraction by the *t*-butoxy radical:

$$t\text{-BuO}\cdot + t\text{-BuO—O—}\underset{CH_3}{\overset{CH_3}{\underset{|}{\overset{|}{C}}}}\text{—}CH_3 \longrightarrow t\text{-BuOH} + t\text{-BuO—O—}\underset{CH_3}{\overset{\cdot CH_2}{\underset{|}{\overset{|}{C}}}}\text{—}CH_3$$

I

The formation of isobutylene oxide is best explained as an intramolecular displacement on the O—O bond in radical I:

$$t\text{-Bu—O—O—}\underset{CH_3}{\overset{\cdot CH_2}{\underset{|}{\overset{|}{C}}}}\text{—}CH_3 \longrightarrow t\text{-BuO}\cdot + \text{O—}\underset{CH_3}{\overset{CH_2}{\underset{|}{\overset{|}{C}}}}\text{—}CH_3 \qquad (3\text{-}4)$$

I

If *t*-butyl peroxide is decomposed in the presence of an active hydrogen donor AH, the methyl and *t*-butoxy radicals can react by abstracting hydrogen from AH. Under these circumstances, the yields of methane and of *t*-butyl alcohol are greatly increased:

$$t\text{-BuO}\cdot \longrightarrow CH_3\text{—}\overset{O}{\overset{\|}{C}}\text{—}CH_3 + \cdot CH_3 \qquad (3\text{-}5)$$

$$t\text{-BuO}\cdot + AH \longrightarrow t\text{-BuOH} + A\cdot \qquad (3\text{-}6)$$

$$CH_3\cdot + AH \longrightarrow CH_4 + A\cdot \qquad (3\text{-}7)$$

$$2CH_3\cdot \longrightarrow C_2H_6 \qquad (3\text{-}8)$$

These reactions have been used to compare the hydrogen donating abilities of various solvents: if the yields of *t*-butyl alcohol and acetone are compared, the ratio of the rate of Reaction (3-6) to (3-5) may be determined. Similarly, the ratio of methane to ethane gives the ratio of the rates of Reactions (3-7) and (3-8). Qualitatively, the alcohol/acetone and methane/ethane ratios increase as the solvent AH becomes a better hydrogen donor.

3.3 ACETYL PEROXIDE

Acetyl peroxide decomposes to produce methane, ethane, carbon dioxide, and methyl acetate. These products can be explained in terms of the following mechanism, where AH is any hydrogen donor, radicals in brackets are cage radicals (see below), and other radicals are separated from one another by solvent molecules:

$$CH_3-\overset{\overset{O}{\|}}{C}-O-O-\overset{\overset{O}{\|}}{C}-CH_3 \begin{cases} \longrightarrow 2CH_3-CO_2\cdot \longrightarrow 2CH_3\cdot + 2CO_2 & (3\text{-}9a) \\ \longrightarrow [CH_3-CO_2\cdot \quad \cdot O_2C-CH_3] & (3\text{-}9b) \end{cases}$$

$$[2CH_3-CO_2\cdot] \longrightarrow 2CH_3-CO_2\cdot \tag{3-10}$$

$$CH_3-CO_2\cdot \longrightarrow CH_3\cdot + CO_2 \tag{3-11}$$

$$CH_3\cdot + AH \longrightarrow CH_4 + A\cdot \tag{3-12}$$

$$2CH_3\cdot \longrightarrow C_2H_6 \tag{3-13}$$

$$[2CH_3-CO_2\cdot] \longrightarrow CH_3-\overset{\overset{O}{\|}}{C}-O-CH_3 + CO_2 \tag{3-14}$$

$$[2CH_3-CO_2\cdot] \longrightarrow C_2H_6 + 2CO_2 \tag{3-15}$$

Acetyl peroxide dissociates to form acetate radicals, Reaction (3-9a). In the gas phase, these acetate radicals lose carbon dioxide by β-scission faster than they undergo any other reaction. However, in solution, the pair of acetate radicals from a given peroxide molecule are held in close proximity by a wall of solvent molecules, Reaction (3-9b). This solvent "cage" holds the original pair of radicals (called the geminate pair) together for about 10^{-10} sec. Once the geminate radicals diffuse into the bulk of the solution, of course, they have an extremely small chance of ever recombining. Thus the solvent cage provides a locus for reactions between geminate pairs which would not be observed in the gas phase. The operational criteria of cage reactions are that they do not occur in the gas phase, and they are not retarded or eliminated by radical scavengers (which can only trap free radicals).

The study of the decomposition of acetyl peroxide in isooctane at 65°C illustrates these features. The yield of carbon dioxide per mole of peroxide decomposed is 1.81 for a 1.3×10^{-3} *M* solution of peroxide. This ratio is not changed if iodine, quinone, or styrene is added as a radical scavenger. Obviously, this ratio would be 2.0 if Reaction (3-9a) were the only reaction which occurred. The missing carbon dioxide implies that a 20% yield of methyl acetate is produced; since the yield of ester is not affected by scavengers, it must be concluded that the ester is formed entirely in the cage, Reaction (3-14). The yield of methane is large (0.82 mole/mole of CO_2 formed), but is reduced to almost zero by 7 *M* styrene. Thus, methane is largely produced from scavengeable free radicals outside the cage; it must arise from the reaction of free methyl radicals with the solvent, Reaction (3-12). The yield of ethane is small (0.02 mole/mole of CO_2 formed), but is not decreased by the addition of styrene. Therefore, most of the ethane must be formed in the cage, Reaction (3-15). In conclusion, methyl acetate and ethane are formed in cage reactions, but methane is formed from the reaction of free methyl radicals with the solvent.

3.4 BENZOYL PEROXIDE

Benzoyl peroxide is perhaps the most commonly used peroxide. In inert solvents, the rate of peroxide disappearance is first order in any one run, but larger rate constants are obtained in concentrated than in dilute solutions. This indicates that both a unimolecular and an induced decomposition occur, since more induced decomposition would be expected to be observed in concentrated solutions where the concentration of radicals is greater.

Since both a unimolecular and an induced decomposition occur, the observed rate will be due to both of these processes. The most convenient way of isolating the unimolecular decomposition for study is to allow the peroxide to decompose in the presence of inhibitors which suppress the induced decomposition. The decomposition in dioxane, for example, has a half-life of 23 min at 80°C and is not first order. However, if iodine, styrene, dichlorostyrene, trinitrobenzene, or any of several other inhibitors is added to the dioxane, the decomposition becomes first order and slows to a half-life of 270 min. It is clear that the induced decomposition is suppressed by effective inhibitors. If the rates of decomposition of a series of ring-substituted benzoyl peroxides are measured in dioxane containing 3,4-dichlorostyrene, the effect of substituents on the unimolecular decomposition can be measured without complications arising from the induced decomposition. Table 3-2 gives the relative rate constants for the unimolecular decomposition of substituted benzoyl peroxides under these conditions. Notice that the electronic effects of substituents are small relative to those observed in many ionic reactions. The data show that electron-donating substituents slightly increase the rate of the dissociation and electron-withdrawing substituents retard it. Electron-donating groups increase the dissociation rate since they increase the electronegativity difference between the peroxide oxygens and the aromatic ring. The greater negative charge on the oxygens produces a larger electrostatic repulsive force between them and a faster rate of dissociation.

Electron displacement caused by electron-donating X,Y-groups:

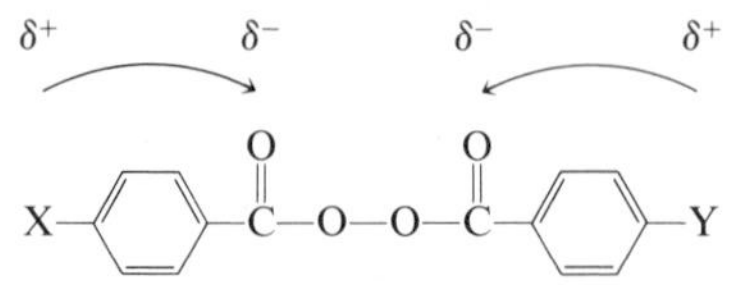

$$\delta^+ \quad \delta^- \quad \delta^- \quad \delta^+$$

$$X-C_6H_4-\overset{\overset{\displaystyle O}{\|}}{C}-O-O-\overset{\overset{\displaystyle O}{\|}}{C}-C_6H_4-Y$$

Table 3-2

THE EFFECT OF SUBSTITUENTS ON THE RATE OF DECOMPOSITION OF BENZOYL PEROXIDES AT 80°C IN DIOXANE (CONTAINING ADDED INHIBITOR)

$$X-C_6H_4-\overset{O}{\overset{\|}{C}}-O-O-\overset{O}{\overset{\|}{C}}-C_6H_4-Y$$

X	Y	Relative rate constant
CH_3O	CH_3O	2.8
CH_3O	H	1.8
CH_3	CH_3	1.5
H	H	1.0
Cl	Cl	0.86

The decomposition of benzoyl peroxide is accelerated by amines, and tertiary amines are often used as cocatalysts in polymerization formulae. This is an example of radical formation being facilitated by substances which might normally be considered ionic catalysts. The effect can be very striking: a 0.01 *M* solution of benzoyl peroxide has a half-life of 60,000 hr at 20°C. The addition of 0.01 *M* dimethylaniline reduces the half-life to 13 min. We will discuss this phenomenon later in this chapter.

3.5 PERESTERS

Peresters and peracids are related in the same way as ordinary esters and acids:

$$\underset{\text{peracid}}{R-\overset{O}{\overset{\|}{C}}-O-OH} \qquad \underset{\text{perester}}{R-\overset{O}{\overset{\|}{C}}-O-O-R'}$$

Table 3-3 gives examples of peresters and their half-lives for homolysis at 60°C.

Several different modes of decomposition have been identified for peresters, as is shown below:

$$R-\overset{O}{\overset{\|}{C}}-O-O-CR'_3 \begin{cases} \xrightarrow{a} R-\overset{O}{\overset{\|}{C}}O\cdot + \cdot OCR'_3 \\ \xrightarrow{b} R\cdot + CO_2 + \cdot OCR'_3 \\ \xrightarrow{c} A-O-\overset{O}{\overset{\|}{C}}-R + \cdot OCR'_3 \\ \xrightarrow{d} R-\overset{O}{\overset{\|}{C}}-O-\underset{\underset{R'}{|}}{\underset{O}{\underset{|}{C}}}R'_2 \quad \text{(an ionic decomposition reaction)} \end{cases}$$

Path *a* is a simple scission of the O—O bond analogous to that which would occur in peroxides. Path *b* is a simultaneous scission of both the O—O bond and the C—C bond, splitting out carbon dioxide somewhat as nitrogen is split from an azo compound. Path *c* is an induced decomposition by the radical A·. In addition to these three radical decomposition mechanisms, the ionic decomposition shown in *d* has been identified for some peresters. It is the sole decomposition mode for *t*-butyl pertosylate; in methanol as solvent the products are toluenesulfonic acid and acetone dimethyl ketal:

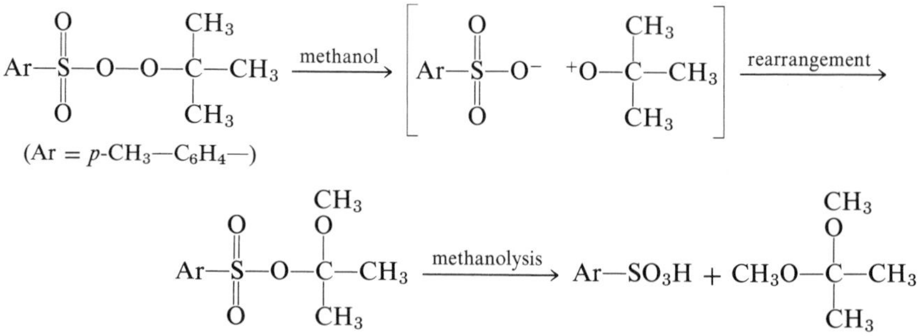

$$Ar{-}\overset{\overset{O}{\|}}{\underset{\underset{O}{\|}}{S}}{-}O{-}O{-}\overset{\overset{CH_3}{|}}{\underset{\underset{CH_3}{|}}{C}}{-}CH_3 \xrightarrow{\text{methanol}} \left[Ar{-}\overset{\overset{O}{\|}}{\underset{\underset{O}{\|}}{S}}{-}O^- \quad {}^+O{-}\overset{\overset{CH_3}{|}}{\underset{\underset{CH_3}{|}}{C}}{-}CH_3 \right] \xrightarrow{\text{rearrangement}}$$

$(Ar = p\text{-}CH_3{-}C_6H_4{-})$

$$Ar{-}\overset{\overset{O}{\|}}{\underset{\underset{O}{\|}}{S}}{-}O{-}\overset{\overset{\overset{CH_3}{O}}{|}}{\underset{\underset{CH_3}{|}}{C}}{-}CH_3 \xrightarrow{\text{methanolysis}} Ar{-}SO_3H + CH_3O{-}\overset{\overset{\overset{CH_3}{O}}{|}}{\underset{\underset{CH_3}{|}}{C}}{-}CH_3$$

The half-lives given in Table 3-3 reveal an interesting feature about the decompositions of these peresters: they have a shorter half-life (that is, they decompose at a faster rate) as the R group is varied so as to form a more stable radical. For example, as R is varied from CH_3 to ϕCH_2 to ϕ_2CH, the rate of dissociation increases smoothly. This suggests that the stability of the R group as a free radical affects the rate of the O—O bond scission. We can explain this by postulating that peresters with R groups which would form relatively stable radicals undergo a synchronous scission of two bonds so that some of the odd electron density is localized on the R group at the transition state. For example, the data in Table 3-3 show that *t*-butyl peracetate and perbenzoate decompose at almost the same rate and that these compounds are the most stable peresters listed. In these compounds, R is methyl and phenyl, respectively, and neither of these groups forms a particularly stable

Table 3-3

PERESTERS AND THE HALF-LIVES OF THEIR DECOMPOSITION REACTIONS

$$t\text{-}BuO{-}O{-}\overset{\overset{O}{\|}}{C}{-}R$$

R	Half-life at 60°C, (min)
$CH_3{-}$	5×10^5
$\phi{-}$	3×10^5
$\phi{-}CH_2{-}$	1.7×10^3
$\phi_2CH{-}$	26
$\phi{-}\overset{\overset{CH_3}{\mid}}{\underset{\underset{CH_3}{\mid}}{C}}{-}$	12
$\phi_2\overset{\overset{CH_3}{\mid}}{C}{-}$	6

radical. These two peresters, therefore, decompose with a simple O—O bond scission:

$$t\text{-BuO—O—CO—CH}_3 \longrightarrow t\text{-BuO}\cdot + \text{CH}_3\text{—CO—O}\cdot$$

$$t\text{-BuO—O—CO—}\phi \longrightarrow t\text{-BuO}\cdot + \phi\text{—CO—O}\cdot$$

However, note that *t*-butyl perphenylacetate decomposes 10^2 times faster than the peracetate or perbenzoate. In this case, the decomposition is postulated to occur by scission of two bonds to produce a benzyl free radical:

$$t\text{-BuO—O—CO—CH}_2\phi \longrightarrow \underset{\text{transition state}}{[t\text{-BuO}\cdots\text{CO}_2\cdots\text{CH}_2\phi]} \longrightarrow t\text{-BuO}\cdot + \text{CO}_2 + \phi\dot{\text{C}}\text{H}_2$$

The localization of some of the odd electron density on the benzyl carbon in the transition state leads to a pronounced rate enhancement. This decomposition may seem unusual at first sight, but it is no more unusual than the splitting out of nitrogen in the dissociation of azo compounds. Compare, for example, this azo compound and perester:

$$\phi\text{—N=N—CH}\phi_2 \longrightarrow \phi\cdot + \text{N}_2 + \cdot\text{CH}\phi_2$$

$$t\text{-BuO—O—CO—CH}\phi_2 \longrightarrow t\text{-BuO}\cdot + \text{CO}_2 + \cdot\text{CH}\phi_2$$

At 60°C, the azo compound has a half-life of about 60 min and the perester has a half-life of 26 min.

3.6 AZO COMPOUNDS

The most useful class of initiators after the peroxides is the class of nitrogen-containing molecules called azo compounds. These compounds dramatically exemplify the effect that the stability of the radical being produced has on the rate of decomposition of a substance. Azomethane, $CH_3\text{—N=N—}CH_3$, decomposes with an activation energy of 51 kcal/mole, and undergoes thermal homolysis at useful rates only at temperatures near 400°C. Table 3-4 gives the activation energies for other azo compounds. Those which produce stabilized radicals decompose at enhanced rates; for example, phenylazotriphenylmethane, $\phi_3\text{C—N=N—}\phi$, decomposes with an activation energy of 27 kcal/mole and is useful at temperatures of 45° to 80°C.

The C—N bond and N=N double bond are of normal strengths (70 and 100 kcal/mole, respectively) and do not suggest that azo compounds would be useful initiators. However, the formation of a molecule of nitrogen in the dissociation of azo compounds provides a strong driving force for dissociation. (The heat of formation of N_2 is 225 kcal/mole.) If the

Table 3-4

AZO COMPOUNDS

R—N=N—R′

R	R′	E_a (kcal/mole)	Solvent
CH_3—	CH_3—	51	Gas phase
t-Bu—	*t*-Bu—	43	Gas phase
ϕ_2CH—	ϕ_2CH—	27	Toluene
ϕ—	ϕ_3C—	27	Benzene
CH_3—C(CN)(CH_3)—	CH_3—C(CN)(CH_3)—	31	Benzene

stability of the nitrogen molecule is to influence the rate of decomposition of an azo compound, then it must be partly formed at the transition state:

$$R{-}N{=}N{-}R \longrightarrow \underset{\text{transition state}}{[R\cdots N{\equiv}N\cdots R]} \longrightarrow 2R\cdot + N_2$$

This transition state also places some of the odd electron density on the R groups and makes clear why the stability of R as a radical influences the rate of decomposition.

The most commonly used azo initiator is azoisobutyronitrile (AIBN), the last compound listed in Table 3-4:

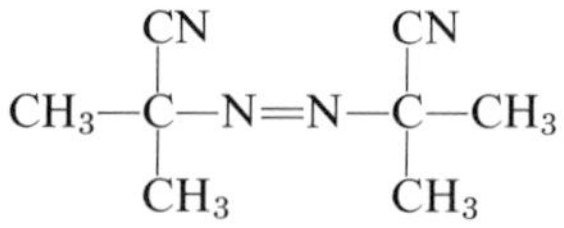

$$CH_3{-}\overset{CN}{\underset{CH_3}{C}}{-}N{=}N{-}\overset{CN}{\underset{CH_3}{C}}{-}CH_3$$

AIBN

AIBN has a half-life of 17 hr at 60°C and 1.3 hr at 80°C, and decomposes at almost the same rate in benzene, toluene, xylene, acetic acid, aniline, nitrobenzene, dodecyl mercaptan, and isobutyl alcohol. It contrasts very markedly with benzoyl peroxide, for example, which has a rate of decomposition that is very dependent on the solvent. Furthermore, the rate of decomposition of AIBN in such solvents as toluene is essentially unaffected by inhibitors such as chloranil, iodine, or DPPH (see p. 7 for structure). This implies that radicals do not attack the azo compound; if they did, the rate of its disappearance would be observed to be lower in the presence of substances that would inhibit the radical chain decomposition. Induced decomposition of most azo compounds is negligible, and for this reason they are sometimes the preferred initiator in studies of radical reactions.

Careful studies of the decomposition reactions of azo compounds have shown the existence of an appreciable cage effect, the details of which have been most thoroughly worked out in the case of AIBN. This initiator is less than 100% efficient in the production of radicals. That is, instead of producing two radicals per mole as would be predicted from the simple decomposition shown below, measurably less than this are formed:

$$R{-}N{=}N{-}R \longrightarrow 2R\cdot + N_2 \tag{3-16}$$

This is because an appreciable fraction of the radicals recombine in the solvent cage before they can diffuse apart. The decomposition of AIBN is complicated by the fact that the cyanopropyl radicals combine to form two termination products, tetramethylsuccinonitrile (R—R) and a ketenimine (R—R′):

$$2H_3C{-}\overset{\displaystyle CN}{\underset{\displaystyle CH_3}{C}}\cdot \;\begin{cases} \nearrow\; CH_3{-}\overset{CN}{\underset{CH_3}{C}}{-}\overset{CN}{\underset{CH_3}{C}}{-}CH_3 \quad (R{-}R) \\ \searrow\; CH_3{-}\overset{CN}{\underset{CH_3}{C}}{-}N{=}C{=}C(CH_3)_2 \quad (R{-}R') \end{cases}$$

Furthermore, the radicals combine to form these two products both in the cage and in solution. Therefore, the decomposition of AIBN must include these reactions:

$$R{-}N{=}N{-}R \longrightarrow [2R\cdot] \longrightarrow 2R\cdot \tag{3-17}$$

$$[2R\cdot] \rightarrow R{-}R,\ R{-}R'; \qquad 2R\cdot \rightarrow R{-}R,\ R{-}R'$$

In this scheme, R· is the cyanopropyl radical, square brackets represent caged radicals, R—R is the succinonitrile and R—R′ is the ketenimine. Note that both the caged and the free cyanopropyl radicals are postulated to give both products. One additional complication exists: although the succinonitrile is a stable product, the ketenimine is not. In fact, the ketenimine is an initiator which decomposes at a rate about that of AIBN itself. Therefore, the complete scheme for the decomposition of AIBN is more complex than shown above.

The scheme given in (3-17) shows two pathways for the formation of tetramethylsuccinonitrile, R—R, one from cage radicals and one from free radicals. This leads to the prediction that scavengers that trap all *free*

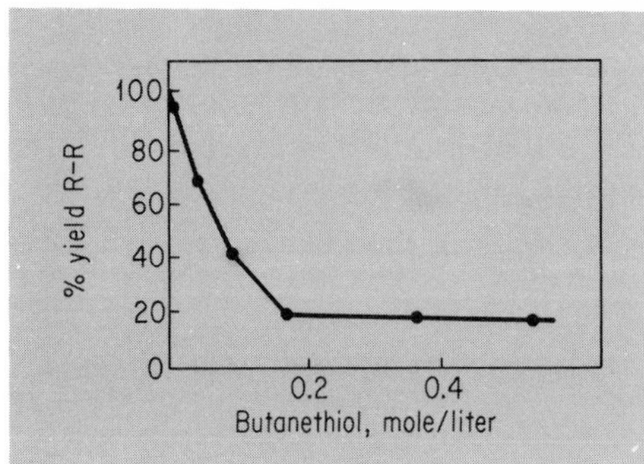

Fig. 3-1 Effect of the concentration of butanethiol on the yield of tetramethylsuccinonitrile. (*J. Am. Chem. Soc.*, reprinted by permission.)

radicals should reduce the yield of R—R to a limiting value that would represent the amount of R—R formed directly in the cage. This effect has been demonstrated with a wide range of scavengers. For example, thiols are very effective hydrogen donors and rapidly react with radicals. Figure 3-1 shows the effect of butanethiol on the yield of tetramethylsuccinonitrile, R—R. As more thiol is added, the yield of succinonitrile rapidly decreases until it levels off at about 20%. This implies that AIBN undergoes approximately 20% cage recombination; that is, it is 80% efficient in producing free radicals in this system.

3.7 HYDROGEN PEROXIDE AND ORGANIC HYDROPEROXIDES

Hydrogen peroxide yields hydroxyl radicals either upon heating or upon irradiation:

$$H_2O_2 \xrightarrow[\text{heat}]{\text{light or}} 2OH\cdot$$

The decomposition of hydrogen peroxide can be catalyzed by iron. A mixture of ferrous ion, hydrogen peroxide, and acid is called Fenton's reagent, and is widely used as an oxidant and a source of hydroxyl radicals:

$$H_2O_2 + Fe^{++} + H^+ \longrightarrow H_2O + \cdot OH + Fe^{+++}$$

These reactions will be discussed further in Chap. 5.

Organic hydroperoxides decompose analogously to hydrogen peroxide to yield hydroxyl radicals, and the decompositions of hydroperoxides also are catalyzed by ferrous ion:

$$ROOH \xrightarrow[\text{heat}]{\text{light or}} RO\cdot + \cdot OH$$

$$ROOH + Fe^{++} \longrightarrow RO\cdot + OH^- + Fe^{+++}$$

The decomposition of *t*-butyl hydroperoxide, either pure or in inert solvents such as chlorobenzene, gives oxygen and *t*-butyl alcohol. The mechanism is:

Initiation:

$$t\text{-BuOOH} \longrightarrow t\text{-BuO}\cdot + \cdot\text{OH}$$

Chain:

$$t\text{-BuO}\cdot + t\text{-BuOOH} \longrightarrow t\text{-BuOH} + t\text{-BuOO}\cdot$$

$$2t\text{-BuOO}\cdot \longrightarrow [t\text{-BuOO—OOBu-}t] \longrightarrow 2t\text{-BuO}\cdot + \text{O}_2$$

t-Butyl hydroperoxide decomposes at an enhanced rate in alcohols, ethers, and amines. These are all solvents which form radicals easily, and the increased hydroperoxide decomposition rate can be attributed to solvent radicals which take part in the induced decomposition. The decomposition then has the following mechanism (*S*H is a solvent molecule with a labile hydrogen):

$$t\text{-BuO}\cdot + S\text{H} \longrightarrow t\text{-BuOH} + S\cdot$$

$$S\cdot + \text{ROOH} \longrightarrow t\text{-BuOO}\cdot + S\text{H}$$

$$2t\text{-BuOO}\cdot \longrightarrow 2t\text{-BuO}\cdot + \text{O}_2$$

Radicals from *t*-butyl hydroperoxide are capable of initiating the polymerization of monomers such as styrene:

$$\text{ROOH} \longrightarrow \text{RO}\cdot + \cdot\text{OH}$$

$$\text{RO}\cdot + \text{M} \longrightarrow \text{RO—M}\cdot \xrightarrow{n\,\text{M}} \text{RO—M}_n\cdot$$

where M represents a molecule of styrene and $\text{RO—M}_n\cdot$ is a polymeric radical. The growing polystyryl radical is able to attack the hydroperoxide, and this adds an induced decomposition pathway to the rate of disappearance of the hydroperoxide:

$$\text{RO—M}_n\cdot + \text{ROOH} \longrightarrow \text{RO—M}_n\text{—H} + \text{ROO}\cdot$$

Thus, the hydroperoxide would be expected to decompose at a faster *total* rate in styrene than in a solvent in which induced decomposition does not occur. This is indeed observed, but there is also an unexpected feature of the decomposition in styrene solution. Kinetic analysis of the system allows separation of the apparently first order and the induced decomposition rates, and it is found that the first order rate, as well as the total rate, is faster than expected. *The presence of styrene causes the unimolecular decomposition of t-butyl hydroperoxide to occur at an unexpectedly rapid rate.* This phenomenon, called molecule-induced homolysis, is discussed in the next section.

3.8 MOLECULE-INDUCED HOMOLYSIS

Molecule-induced homolysis is postulated to occur whenever radicals are formed at an anomalously rapid rate from the interaction of non-radical species; most, but not all examples involve the interaction of olefin solvents with initiators. Molecule-induced homolysis is frequently accompanied by a catalyzed *ionic decomposition* of the initiator, which further complicates the interpretation of the reactions. We will refer to this accompanying ionic reaction when we discuss the mechanism of these processes.

Detailed study of the styrene/*t*-butyl hydroperoxide system discussed in the previous section has shown that the peroxide decomposes by three pathways: an ionic decomposition, an induced decomposition, and an apparently first order decomposition.† The first order decomposition is difficult to isolate and study, but it can be shown that it occurs faster in styrene than in inert solvents. However, because of the complexities of this system, the mechanism by which styrene increases the rate of this first order decomposition is not known.

A molecule-induced homolysis also occurs in the reaction of iodine with styrene. Molecular iodine and styrene interact at 25°C to produce radicals at a rate which is 10^6 times larger than can be explained by homolysis of iodine. This interaction mechanism is second order in styrene and first order in iodine, and could involve a reaction such as

$$2\phi CH{=}CH_2 + I_2 \longrightarrow 2\phi\dot{C}H{-}CH_2I$$

Apparently, the polarizability of the solvent plays a role in determining its effectiveness in inducing homolysis. The decomposition rate of *o*-nitrobenzoyl peroxide in the very polarizable solvent methyl iodide is 300 times greater than that of the peroxide in chloroform. A related phenomenon is the increased rate of homolysis of the O—O bond in the perester shown below:

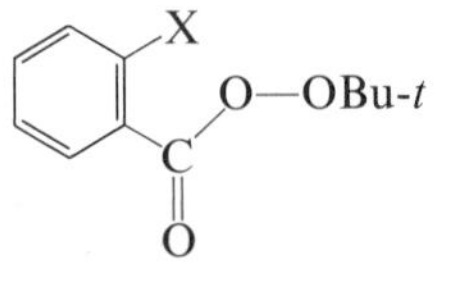

X
O—OBu-*t*
C
O

The relative rate constants for decomposition of this perester at 60°C are:

X	Relative decomposition rate constants
H—	1
t-Bu—	4
I—	54
CH_3S—	1×10^4
ϕS—	2×10^4

† It is necessary to distinguish between *induced* and *molecule-induced decompositions.* An induced decomposition is a *propagation* reaction in which *radicals* attack an initiator molecule and cause its destruction (see, e.g., p. 20). A *molecule-induced* decomposition is an *initiation* process which is accelerated by certain *solvent molecules.*

Apparently very polarizable neighboring atoms enhance the O—O bond scission by an intramolecular molecule-induced homolysis.

Molecule-induced homolysis can be explained in general terms by the following mechanistic scheme. When an initiator A-B undergoes a purely unimolecular dissociation, the activation energy is equal to the A—B bond dissociation energy:

$$A{-}B \longrightarrow A\cdot + B\cdot$$
$$D(A{-}B) = E_a = \Delta H$$

This process is shown as the solid line in Fig. 3-2. If this decomposition occurs in a solvent S which is able to complex with or partially bond to the A· and B· radicals in the transition state, then some of the energy for bond scission is supplied by the heat released during the formation of the partial S--A and S--B bonds. This process is shown as the dashed line in Fig. 3-2 and can be represented by the equation below:

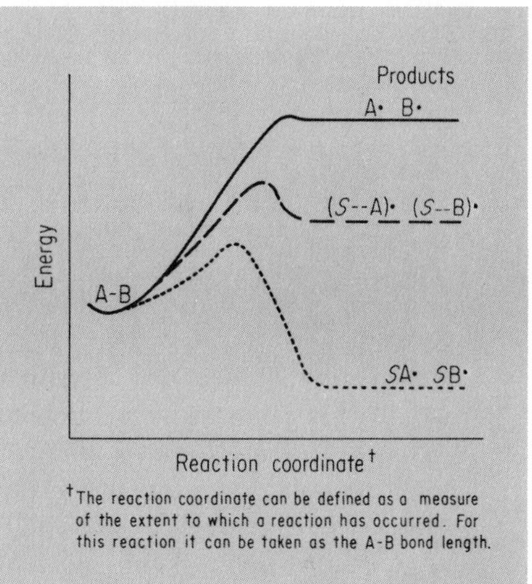

Fig. 3-2 Reaction coordinate versus energy diagram for the unassisted homolysis of A—B, and for homolysis in the solvent S which complexes with or bonds to the radical fragments.

$$A{-}B + 2S \longrightarrow (S{-}{-}A)\cdot + (S{-}{-}B)\cdot$$

In the limiting case, the solvent S bonds to A· or B·, or both, and the heat of reaction is reduced by the bond energy of the A—S and B—S bonds [See Eq. (1-7), p. 11]:

$$A{-}B + 2S \longrightarrow SA\cdot + SB\cdot$$
$$\Delta H = D(A{-}B) - D(S{-}A) - D(S{-}B)$$

If the formation of the S—A and S—B bonds releases more energy than is required to break the A—B bond, then the bond dissociation process will be exothermic (that is, ΔH be negative), and the activation energy should be greatly reduced. This is shown as a dotted line in Fig. 3-2.

It is instructive to calculate the amount of energy which is available to aid in the dissociation of a particular initiator. Consider the very simple model system consisting of chlorine in ethylene. The value of D(Cl—Cl) is 58 kcal/mole, and the addition of a chlorine atom to ethylene is exothermic by about 26 kcal/mole:

	ΔH (kcal/mole)
$Cl_2 \longrightarrow 2Cl\cdot$	58
$Cl\cdot + CH_2{=}CH_2 \longrightarrow ClCH_2{-}\dot{C}H_2$	-26

Therefore the heat of the molecule-induced decomposition of chlorine in ethylene could be reduced to as low as 6 kcal/mole, as shown below:

$$Cl_2 + 2CH_2{=}CH_2 \longrightarrow 2ClCH_2{-}\dot{C}H_2 \qquad \Delta H = 58 - 2(26) = 6 \text{ kcal/mole}$$

Thus, although the dissociation of chlorine is highly endothermic and would only occur at measurable rates at high temperatures, the molecule-induced decomposition is almost thermally neutral; it might be expected to have a low activation energy and to occur at a moderate rate near room temperature. In fact, as we shall see in Chap. 7, many olefins undergo spontaneous free radical chlorination at room temperature as a result of molecule-induced decompositions.

One further feature of these molecule-induced decompositions should be pointed out. The mechanisms we have considered all involve electron donation from a polarizable solvent to an electron-accepting radical. As the solvent becomes a better electron-donor and as the radical fragments become more electronegative, we can expect this electron donation to approach a complete transfer of electrons from the solvent to the radical. This can be represented as a polar structure for the transition state such as that shown below:

$$S{:}\curvearrowright A{-}B \longrightarrow \underset{\text{transition state}}{[SA\cdot \quad \cdot B \longleftrightarrow SA^{+} \quad ^{-}{:}B]}$$

If the electrons are fully transferred, the reaction becomes an SN2 displacement at the A—B bond by the nucleophilic solvent S:

$$S{:}\curvearrowright + A{\frown}B \longrightarrow SA^{+} + {}^{-}{:}B$$

It is now clear why electron-rich olefins and electronegative initiators such as the halogens are particularly susceptible to molecule-induced decompositions. This also explains why nucleophilic species sometimes cause the dissociation of peroxides at enhanced rates. For example, the transition state for the reaction of dimethylaniline and benzoyl peroxide discussed on page 24 might be represented as below:

$$R_3N{:} + \phi{-}\overset{O}{\overset{\|}{C}}{-}O{-}O{-}\overset{O}{\overset{\|}{C}}{-}\phi \longrightarrow \underset{\text{transition state}}{\left[\begin{matrix} R_3N{:}\curvearrowright O & {:}\curvearrowright O \\ | & | \\ CO & CO \\ | & | \\ \phi & \phi \end{matrix} \longleftrightarrow \begin{matrix} R_3N^{\pm}{-}O & ^{-}{:}O \\ | & | \\ CO & CO \\ | & | \\ \phi & \phi \end{matrix}\right]}$$

Some separation of charge has been shown in the transition states discussed in this section. These charge-separated forms for transition states imply that radical reactions could show polar effects of the type observed in ionic reactions, and this is frequently the case. We shall discuss examples of this in Sec. 6.3.

PROBLEMS

1. Explain why CH_3—O—O—CH_3 and *t*-Bu—O—O—Bu-*t* both have approximately the same activation energy for decomposition (37 kcal/mole) whereas the activation energies for decomposition of CH_3—N=N—CH_3 and *t*-Bu—N=N—Bu-*t* are 51 and 43 kcal/mole respectively.

2. Write the reactions which occur when *t*-butyl peroxide decomposes in a solvent *S*H that is a moderate hydrogen donor. List all the equations you write under one of these headings: initiation, propagation, or termination. Be sure you include a reaction which produces acetone as a product. How would the ratio of the yields of acetone to *t*-butyl alcohol change if the solvent *S*H were replaced with a better hydrogen donor?

3. Give operational criteria for distinguishing a product produced in a cage reaction from one produced in a non-cage process. How could you distinguish between cage products and those formed in non-radical processes in the free solution?

4. In the decomposition of acetyl peroxide in the solvent *S*H, methane and ethane are both produced. Write the reactions which are chiefly responsible for the production of each of these products. Be careful to distinguish between cage and non-cage processes.

5. The data on the decomposition of *t*-butyl peroxide in the pure peroxide (p. 21) show that the yield of methane plus twice the yield of ethane equals the yield of acetone. Give a mechanism which explains this.

6. Rationalize the more rapid rate of decomposition of

$$\phi_2CH—CO—O—OBu\text{-}t$$

relative to CH_3—CO—O—OBu-*t* at 60°C.

7. Suggest a detailed mechanism for the reaction in which *m,m′*-dibromobenzoyl peroxide and *p,p′*-dimethoxystilbene interact in benzene solution to produce radicals at a more rapid rate than the peroxide alone would dissociate. Why would this particular peroxide and olefin pair be particularly susceptible to molecule-induced homolysis?

8. Write a transition state for the dissociation of *t*-butyl *o*-iodoperbenzoate which rationalizes its more rapid rate of decomposition relative to *t*-butyl perbenzoate.

9. Discuss Fig. 3-1. Explain why the yield of the succinonitrile product decreases as the thiol concentration increases. Why does the product yield reach a limiting value?

10. Draw resonance structures for the transition state for the decomposition of

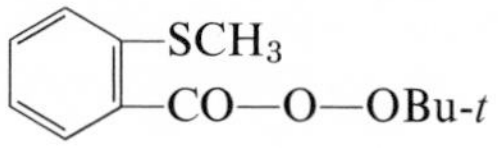

$$o\text{-}C_6H_4(SCH_3)\text{—CO—O—OBu-}t$$

Can the enhanced rate of decomposition of this perester relative to the unsubstituted compound be explained as a steric effect? Explain.

11. Suggest two possible mechanisms for the induced decomposition of benzoyl peroxide by R· radicals. When benzoyl peroxide labeled in the carbonyl group with O-18 is used, $RO\text{—}\overset{O^{18}}{\overset{\|}{C}}\phi$ is obtained. Does this allow a choice to be made between your two mechanisms?

12. Explain Fig. 3-2. Draw the transition states for the unimolecular dissociation of A—B (the solid line in the figure) and for the molecule-induced decomposition (the dotted line). What is the relationship between the overall heat of the reaction and D(A—B), D(*S*—A), and D(*S*—B)? Explain the differences and similarities between molecule-induced decompositions and SN2 displacements. Distinguish between radical- and molecule-induced decompositions.

4 Photochemical Production of Radicals

The energy necessary to cause bond scission can be supplied by any form of electromagnetic radiation (for example, ultraviolet light, visible light, or x-rays) or corpuscular radiation (for example, high energy electrons, α, β, or γ particles, neutrons, or protons). We will limit our discussion to processes involving light, a subdivision of radiation chemistry called photochemistry.

4.1 INTRODUCTION

We are interested in processes in which the absorption of light leads to homolytic bond scission (homolytic photolysis). However, excitation of molecules by light can be followed by physical, as well as chemical, deexcitation processes; furthermore, all the chemical processes do not necessarily involve free radicals. (Photochemical reactions may be molecular processes or can involve ions.) Thus, we are interested in only a small portion of the total area of photochemistry. However, we must view homolytic photolysis in the context of photoexcitation processes in general, so some discussion of physical and non-radical photochemical processes will be helpful†.

4.2 POSSIBLE REACTIONS OF PHOTOEXCITED SPECIES

Light can be transmitted, refracted, scattered, or absorbed by a system. It is a fundamental tenet of photochemistry that only the light which is absorbed can produce a chemical change. A quantum of light of frequency

† Photochemistry is discussed in more detail in the volume in this series by C. DePuy, *Molecular Reactions and Photochemistry* (in preparation).

ν has an energy given by

$$E = h\nu$$

where h is Planck's constant. A mole of quanta is called an einstein, and has energy equal to $Nh\nu$, where N is Avogadro's number. The relation between the wavelength or frequency of light and the energy associated with one einstein of the light, therefore, is:

$$E = Nh\nu = \frac{Nhc}{\lambda} = \frac{2.859 \times 10^5}{\lambda} \text{ kcal/einstein}$$

where λ is the wavelength of the light in angstroms and c is the velocity of light. Thus, light of 7500 Å wavelength represents 38 kcal/einstein; light of 3130 Å wavelength represents 91 kcal/einstein, enough to cause the scission of carbon-carbon bonds.

When a molecule absorbs a quantum of light, it can lose its excess energy in any of the physical or chemical processes listed below:

Physical processes	Chemical processes
thermal quenching	radical reactions
fluorescence	non-radical reactions
phosphorescence	
internal conversion	

4.3 PHYSICAL DEEXCITATION PROCESSES

Let us consider physical deexcitation processes first. The simplest physical process to envision is quenching, in which the excitation energy is transferred to other molecules present in the system. Quenching occurs both in the gas and liquid phases, and different solvent molecules show different efficiencies as quenchers. For example, in the gas phase, mercury atoms absorb light to form an excited state, Hg*, and various gaseous diluents can quench this excitation. Hydrocarbons are particularly effective quenchers because they can lose the excitation energy in dissociative processes:

$$\text{Hg} + h\nu \longrightarrow \text{Hg}^*$$

$$\text{Hg}^* + \text{RH} \longrightarrow \text{Hg} + \text{R}\cdot + \text{H}\cdot$$

Energy transfer of this type provides a mechanism by which energy can be supplied to molecules which do not themselves absorb the irradiating light. As we shall see, this energy transfer has synthetic utility.

The other physical processes for deexcitation of a molecule can best be understood by using Fig. 4-1. This figure schematically shows several electronic levels and some of the vibrational and rotational sublevels of a typical organic molecule. The electronic levels on the left of the figure are labeled *singlet* levels, while those on the right are labeled *triplet*. In spec-

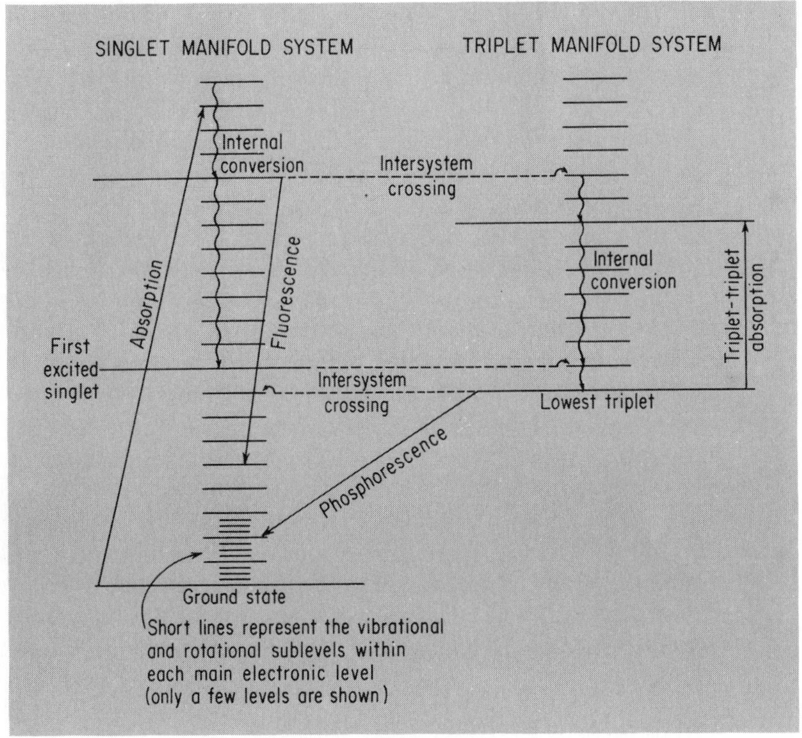

Fig. 4-1 Typical transitions between the energy levels of a generalized organic molecule.

troscopy, the multiplicity of a species is given by $(2S + 1)$, where S is the total electron spin. If only paired electrons are present, all spins cancel, $S = 0$, $2S + 1 = 1$, and the species is a singlet. If two electrons have parallel spins, each with the value of $\frac{1}{2}$, $S = 1$, $2S + 1 = 3$, and the state is a triplet. Triplet species might be expected to have some of the properties of diradicals and to behave like free radicals. Actually, a true diradical would have two electrons of completely independent spin, each with $S = \frac{1}{2}$, and spectroscopically would be a pair of doublets rather than a triplet. The detailed relationship between triplets and diradicals is complex, and beyond the bounds of this text. For our purposes, we can view triplets as one end of a continuum which blends smoothly into true diradicals in physical properties and chemical reactivities. Thus, we can anticipate that many, but not all triplets, will react in ways characteristic of free radicals, such as by hydrogen abstraction, for example.

With this brief background we can examine the processes shown in Fig. 4-1. First, consider the singlet states on the left of the figure. Absorption can be followed by radiationless processes; this shown as wavy arrows representing cascades down vibrational sublevels and internal conversion to lower singlet electronic levels; the energy lost in these processes is quenched by other molecules in the system. Absorption can also be followed by a transition which produces an emission of radiation; such transitions are represented by straight arrows in the figure. Radiative transitions between two states of the same multiplicity are called fluorescence. Since the lifetime of species in excited states is very short, fluorescence occurs within 10^{-9} to 10^{-6} sec after absorption.

Now consider the triplet states shown at the right of Fig. 4-1. Some molecules can decay from an excited singlet to a metastable triplet state. A radiationless transition between states of different multiplicities is called intersystem crossing; these transitions are represented by dashed arrows in the figure. In theory, transitions between states of different multiplicities are forbidden, however, real states are not pure triplets or singlets and so intersystem crossing occurs, but with a lower probability than ordinary internal conversions. The lifetime of a species in the triplet state may be longer than in an excited singlet state, and radiative decay or intersystem crossing from the triplet back to the singlet state may be delayed by 10^{-3} sec or even longer. Any radiative transition between states of different multiplicities is called phosphorescence. In organic molecules, the usual phosphorescence involves that shown in Fig. 4-1, from the lowest excited triplet to a vibrational level of the ground electronic state.

4.4 CHEMICAL DEEXCITATION PROCESSES

We now turn to a consideration of the types of chemical reactions which can follow the excitation of a molecule by light. One of the simplest is photochemical halogenation of a hydrocarbon. For example, consider the photochlorination of the hydrocarbon RH. When chlorine is irradiated with light of wavelength less than 4875 Å, photolysis occurs; if a hydrocarbon RH is present, it becomes halogenated in the usual chain sequence:

$$\begin{aligned} Cl_2 &\xrightarrow{h\nu} Cl_2^* \\ Cl_2^* &\longrightarrow 2Cl\cdot \\ Cl\cdot + RH &\longrightarrow R\cdot + HCl \\ R\cdot + Cl_2 &\longrightarrow RCl + Cl\cdot \end{aligned}$$

where Cl_2^* is a molecule of chlorine which has absorbed a light quantum. The efficiency of photochemical processes in utilizing light energy is expressed as the quantum yield Φ, where Φ is defined as the number of moles of a product produced per einstein of light absorbed. Since the absorbed energy can be lost in physical processes that do not involve chemical reaction, Φ can be zero. On the other extreme, a product may be produced by a chain reaction and Φ can be 10^6 or larger. In chlorinations, each chlorine atom produced in the primary photochemical reaction leads to the eventual formation of a large number of product molecules via the chain sequence shown above, and Φ_{RCl} may be as large as 10^4 to 10^6.

4.5 CARBONYL COMPOUNDS

Much of the early research in photochemistry was done using carbonyl compounds; these compounds have an absorption band near 3200 Å, and light of this wavelength can be conveniently produced using mercury arcs. Furthermore, Pyrex glassware is transparent to 3200 Å light, so the photochemistry of carbonyl compounds can be studied using relatively simple equipment.

Aldehydes can undergo at least four possible photolysis reactions:

$$\mathrm{R{-}CH_2{-}CH_2{-}CHO} \xrightarrow{h\nu} \mathrm{R{-}CH_2{-}\dot{C}H_2} + \mathrm{\cdot CHO}$$

$$\mathrm{R{-}CH_2{-}CH_2{-}CHO} \xrightarrow{h\nu} \mathrm{R{-}CH_2{-}CH_3} + \mathrm{CO}$$

$$\mathrm{R{-}CH_2{-}CH_2{-}CHO} \xrightarrow{h\nu} \mathrm{R{-}CH{=}CH_2} + \mathrm{HCHO}$$

$$\mathrm{R{-}CH_2{-}CH_2{-}CHO} \xrightarrow{h\nu} \mathrm{R{-}\dot{C}H_2} + \mathrm{\cdot CH_2{-}CHO}$$

Note that some of these reactions involve free radicals and some do not. The reactions which occur depend on the structure of the aldehyde and the wavelength of the light used. For example, excitation of butyraldehyde in the gas phase leads to two photolysis reactions; one gives propyl and formyl free radicals, and one gives ethylene and acetaldehyde:

$$\mathrm{CH_3{-}CH_2{-}CH_2{-}CHO} \xrightarrow{h\nu} \mathrm{(CH_3{-}CH_2{-}CH_2{-}CHO)^*}$$

$$\mathrm{(CH_3{-}CH_2{-}CH_2{-}CHO)^*} \longrightarrow \mathrm{CH_3{-}CH_2{-}\dot{C}H_2} + \mathrm{\cdot CHO}$$

$$\mathrm{(CH_3{-}CH_2{-}CH_2{-}CHO)^*} \longrightarrow \mathrm{CH_2{=}CH_2} + \mathrm{CH_3{-}CHO}$$

Ketones also can undergo a variety of photochemical decompositions; for example, acetone reacts to produce acetyl and methyl radicals. The acetyl radicals subsequently undergo β-scission to produce another methyl radical and a molecule of carbon monoxide. The ultimate products are ethane and carbon monoxide as shown below:

$$\mathrm{C_3H_6O} \xrightarrow{h\nu} \mathrm{C_3H_6O^*}$$

$$\mathrm{C_3H_6O^*} \longrightarrow \mathrm{CH_3{-}\overset{\overset{\displaystyle O}{\|}}{C}\cdot} + \mathrm{\cdot CH_3}$$

$$\mathrm{CH_3{-}\overset{\overset{\displaystyle O}{\|}}{C}\cdot} \longrightarrow \mathrm{CO} + \mathrm{\cdot CH_3}$$

$$\mathrm{2CH_3\cdot} \longrightarrow \mathrm{C_2H_6}$$

where $C_3H_6O^*$ is an excited acetone molecule. The quantum yield for carbon monoxide, Φ_{CO}, is found to be 1.0 at 2537 Å, and 0.7 at 3130 Å. The photolysis of acetone has been studied thoroughly and the production of carbon monoxide is frequently used as an internal standard to measure how many photons are being provided to a given reaction system. This reaction also is frequently used as a source of methyl radicals. In the presence of a hydrogen donor AH, the methyl radicals either abstract hydrogen or dimerize to form ethane:

$$CH_3\cdot + AH \longrightarrow CH_4 + A\cdot$$
$$2CH_3\cdot \longrightarrow C_2H_6$$

These reactions can be used to measure the relative hydrogen donating abilities of molecules; qualitatively, more methane will be formed as AH becomes a better hydrogen donor.

Ketones that have one alkyl group that is at least three carbon atoms long may decompose by an intramolecular mechanism which does not involve free radicals. For example, methyl butyl ketone gives acetone and propylene:

$$CH_3{-}\overset{\overset{O}{\|}}{C}{-}CH_2{-}CH_2{-}CH_2{-}CH_3 \xrightarrow{h\nu} CH_3{-}\overset{\overset{O}{\|}}{C}{-}CH_3 + CH_2{=}CH{-}CH_3$$

The quantum yields of olefin and acetone are observed to be almost equal under all experimental conditions, so it is concluded that they are formed in the same primary photochemical process. Other ketones which decompose by this intramolecular process include *di*-propyl ketone, methyl propyl ketone, methyl pentyl ketone, methyl *sec*-butyl ketone, and methyl neopentyl ketone. The most likely mechanism for this decomposition involves the transfer of a γ-hydrogen atom to form an enol and an olefin. This is illustrated below, using methyl butyl ketone as an example:

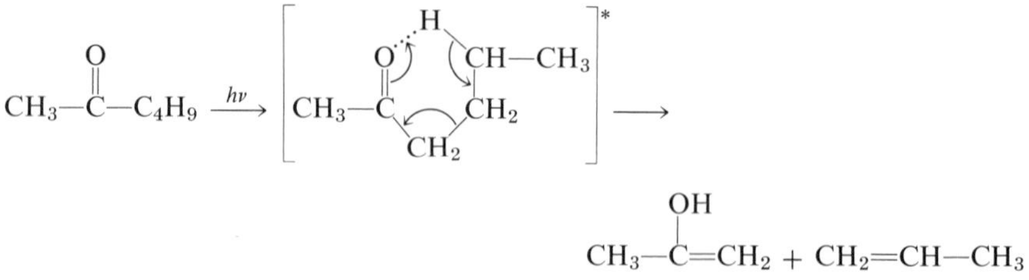

$$CH_3{-}\overset{\overset{O}{\|}}{C}{-}C_4H_9 \xrightarrow{h\nu} \left[CH_3{-}\overset{\overset{O\cdots H}{\|}}{C}\underset{CH_2}{\frown}CH_2{-}CH{-}CH_3 \right]^* \longrightarrow$$

$$CH_3{-}\overset{\overset{OH}{|}}{C}{=}CH_2 + CH_2{=}CH{-}CH_3$$

Radicals may also be produced in more complex photochemical processes. For example, excitation of the dienone shown below leads to splitting out a $\cdot CCl_3$ fragment:

$$\text{4-methyl-4-(trichloromethyl)cyclohexa-2,5-dienone} \xrightarrow[\text{hydrocarbon solvents}]{h\nu} \left[\text{diradical}\right]^* \xrightarrow{\beta\text{-scission}} \text{4-methylphenoxy radical} + \cdot CCl_3 \xrightarrow[SH]{\text{solvent}} \text{p-cresol} + CHCl_3 + Cl_3C{-}CCl_3$$

possible diradical intermediate

4.6 ENERGY TRANSFER

For photoreactions to occur, either the substrate must absorb the irradiating light or some photosensitizer must be used which can absorb the light and efficiently pass the photoexcitation energy to the substrate. This photosensitization process has practical use when the substrate does not have a conveniently accessible absorption band or does not undergo particularly facile intersystem crossing. Aromatic ketones such as benzophenone and acetophenone absorb radiation from mercury arcs and undergo intersystem crossing extremely efficiently to produce their triplet species. Thus, small amounts of these ketones can be used as photosensitizers to produce triplet species that would be hard to produce directly. For example, aldehydes undergo the following radical chain decarbonylation:

Initiation:

$$RCHO \xrightarrow{\text{initiators}} R\dot{C}O$$

Chain:

$$R\dot{C}O \longrightarrow R\cdot + CO$$

$$R\cdot + RCHO \longrightarrow RH + R\dot{C}O$$

Although this decarbonylation can be effected by direct photolysis, small amounts of acetophenone increase the rate by photosensitization. The mechanism of this process is shown below, where $(\phi COCH_3)^*$ is a photoexcited molecule of acetophenone and the subscript s or t stands for a singlet or a triplet state:

$$\phi COCH_3 \xrightarrow[\text{excitation}]{h\nu} (\phi COCH_3)^*_s \xrightarrow[\text{crossing}]{\text{intersystem}} (\phi COCH_3)^*_t$$

$$(\phi COCH_3)^*_t + RCHO \xrightarrow[\text{energy transfer}]{\text{triplet}} \phi COCH_3 + (RCHO)^*_t$$

Initiation:

$$(RCHO)_t^* \longrightarrow R\cdot + \cdot CHO$$

Chain:

$$R\cdot + RCHO \longrightarrow RH + R\dot{C}O$$

$$R\dot{C}O \longrightarrow R\cdot + CO$$

Diolefins are harder to excite to triplet species than are ketones because of a much lower probability for intersystem crossing. For example, cyclopentadiene does not give good yields of the triplet when irradiated. However, if a mixture of benzophenone and cyclopentadiene is irradiated, the triplet state of the ketone is produced, and it transfers its excitation to the diene to give the cyclopentadiene triplet:

$$\phi_2C{=}O \xrightarrow{h\nu} (\phi_2C{=}O)_s^* \xrightarrow[\text{crossing}]{\text{intersystem}} (\phi_2C{=}O)_t^*$$

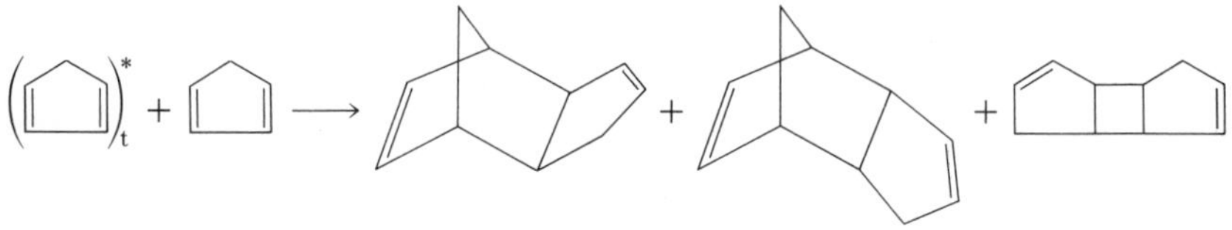

$$(\phi_2C{=}O)_t^* + \text{cyclopentadiene} \longrightarrow \phi_2C{=}O + (\text{cyclopentadiene})_t^*$$

$$(\text{cyclopentadiene})_t^* + \text{cyclopentadiene} \longrightarrow$$

33% *exo* + 33% *endo* + 33%

This result is particularly useful since the direct thermal dimerization of cyclopentadiene by the usual Diels-Alder mechanism leads to a 100% yield of the endo product:

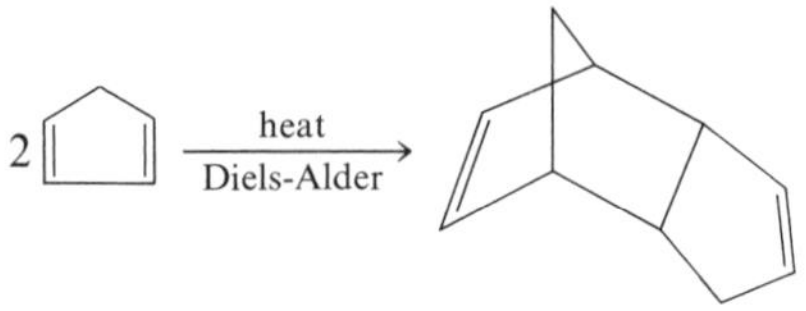

$$2\ \text{cyclopentadiene} \xrightarrow[\text{Diels-Alder}]{\text{heat}}$$

100% *endo*

PROBLEMS

1. How many kcal of energy are contained in 1 einstein of light of 2500 Å?

2. Outline the possible ways in which energy can be lost by a photoexcited molecule. Give an example of each.

3. Quenching is more prevalent in the liquid than in the gas phase. Suggest a reason for this.

4. Define phosphorescence.

5. The quantum yield of carbon monoxide from acetone is 0.7 at 3130 Å. In a particular experiment, 0.5 mole of carbon monoxide is produced in 24 hours. How many einsteins of energy were supplied? How many quanta were absorbed by the acetone per second?

6. Irradiation of a mixture of benzophenone and isopropyl alcohol with 3660 Å light at 25°C gives benzopinacol $\phi_2C(OH)—C(OH)\phi_2$ with a quantum yield of 0.93 and acetone with quantum yield of 0.92. One molecule of acetone is produced for each molecule of benzopinacol formed. If dissolved oxygen is present, the quantum yield of acetone is unchanged, the yield of benzopinacol drops to zero, and H_2O_2 is formed. Propose a mechanism which explains these facts.

7. The chain decarbonylation of aldehydes is photosensitized by acetophenone, and is increased in chain length if thiols are present. Write a detailed mechanism for the photochemical decarbonylation of the aldehyde RCHO in the presence of low concentrations of benzophenone and thiophenol. Assume that only benzophenone absorbs the wavelength of light used.

8. Predict the product(s) of the photolysis of methyl *sec*-butyl ketone.

UGGESTED FURTHER READINGS

Hammond, G. S., and Turro, N. J., "Organic Photochemistry," *Science,* **142**(1963), 1541.

Leermakers, P. A., and Vesley, G. F., "Organic Photochemistry and the Excited State," *J. Chem. Ed.,* **41**(1964), 535.

Moore, W. J., *Physical Chemistry* (3rd ed.). Englewood Cliffs, N.J.: Prentice-Hall, Inc., 1963. See Chap. 21.

5 Radical-Forming Redox Reactions

5.1 GENERAL

Production of radicals by oxidation-reduction reactions offers some advantages over the use of initiators. Since radical production results from reaction between the two members of the redox pair, the rate of radical production can be controlled by varying the concentrations of these two species. This overcomes the limitation of dealing with an initiator which has a characteristic rate of radical production at any given temperature. Also, redox reactions are known which produce radicals at temperatures below the useful range of commercially available initiators.

In redox reactions, radicals can be produced by either oxidation or by reduction. In the Kolbe electrolysis, salts of organic acids are electrolyzed and the carboxylate anions undergo oxidation at the anode to a radical which loses carbon dioxide. The resulting radicals couple:

$$R{-}CO_2^- \xrightarrow[(-e^-)]{\text{anode}} R{-}CO_2\cdot \longrightarrow R\cdot + CO_2$$

$$2R\cdot \longrightarrow R{-}R$$

This reaction has some utility in organic syntheses.

The most important radical-forming redox reactions are those which involve a metal ion that can undergo a one-electron transfer. Of these, the reaction of hydrogen peroxide with ferrous ion, discovered by Fenton in 1894, is one of the oldest and best known. In 1932 Haber and Weiss proposed the mechanism which is accepted today. The main reactions are:

$$Fe^{++} + H_2O_2 \longrightarrow Fe^{+++} + OH^- + \cdot OH \qquad (5\text{-}1)$$

$$Fe^{+++} + H_2O_2 \longrightarrow Fe^{++} + HO_2\cdot + H^+$$

These reactions explain the catalysis of the decomposition of hydrogen peroxide by iron.

$$2H_2O_2 \xrightarrow{\text{iron salts}} 2H_2O + O_2$$

Fenton's reagent can be used to oxidize organic materials. Sometimes the oxidized products are dimers and sometimes they are the result of substitution reactions by hydroxyl radicals. For example, benzene is converted to a mixture of biphenyl and phenol:

$$Fe^{++} + H_2O_2 \longrightarrow Fe^{+++} + OH^- + OH\cdot$$

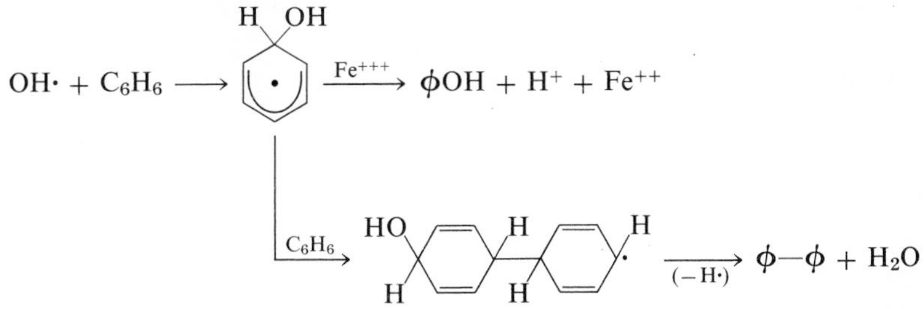

$$OH\cdot + C_6H_6 \longrightarrow \text{(H, OH-cyclohexadienyl radical)} \xrightarrow{Fe^{+++}} \phi OH + H^+ + Fe^{++}$$

$$\text{(H, OH-cyclohexadienyl radical)} \xrightarrow{C_6H_6} \text{HO, H-cyclohexadienyl–cyclohexadienyl radical (H, H, H)} \xrightarrow[(-H\cdot)]{} \phi{-}\phi + H_2O$$

Reaction (5-1) occurs with ions of other metals and with hydroperoxides, peroxides, and peresters, as well as with hydrogen peroxide. The reaction can be formulated generally as:

$$M^{I} + ROOR \longrightarrow M^{II} + RO\cdot + RO^-$$

where M^{I} is a transition metal in one valence state, and M^{II} is the next higher oxidation valence state. Examples of reactions of this type are:

$$H_2O_2 \xrightarrow[V^{++},\text{ or } Ti^{+++}]{Fe^{++}, Cr^{++},} HO\cdot + OH^-$$

$$ROOH \xrightarrow[\text{or } Cu^+]{Fe^{++}, Co^{++},} RO\cdot + OH^-$$

$$RO{-}O{-}\overset{\overset{\displaystyle O}{\|}}{C}{-}R' \xrightarrow{Cu^+} RO\cdot + R'CO_2^-$$

$$^-O_3S{-}O{-}O{-}SO_3^- \xrightarrow{Fe^{++}} SO_4^= + SO_4^-\cdot$$

The most important commercial application of these redox reactions is in the manufacture of synthetic rubber for tires. In this process, a mixture of styrene and butadiene is polymerized at a low temperature using the redox pair cumene hydroperoxide plus ferrous ion.

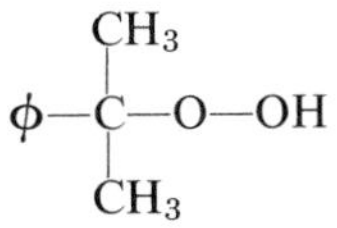

$$\phi{-}\underset{\displaystyle CH_3}{\overset{\displaystyle CH_3}{\underset{|}{\overset{|}{C}}}}{-}O{-}OH$$

cumene hydroperoxide

The organic monomers are polymerized in oil-like droplets in an aqueous emulsion which is maintained by the addition of soaps and bases.

5.2 COPPER-CATALYZED REACTIONS

Another example of a redox reaction that has been developed into a useful synthetic tool is the reaction of peroxidic materials with substrates containing active hydrogens. In the absence of metal ions, a mixture of products is usually obtained. However, metal ions, particularly copper ions, catalyze a reaction so that excellent yields result. An example is the reaction of *t*-butyl peracetate with cyclohexene catalyzed by cuprous bromide:

$$\text{cyclohexene} + CH_3-\overset{O}{\overset{\|}{C}}-O-OBu\text{-}t \xrightarrow{CuBr} \text{3-cyclohexenyl-}O-\overset{O}{\overset{\|}{C}}-CH_3 \quad (90\%) \qquad (5\text{-}2)$$

This is the best synthesis of cyclohexenyl acetate. The mechanism of this reaction is believed to involve the formation of a *t*-butoxy radical from the perester by a Haber-Weiss type decomposition:

$$CH_3-\overset{O}{\overset{\|}{C}}-O-OBu\text{-}t + Cu^{I} \longrightarrow (CH_3-CO_2\cdot Cu^{I}) + t\text{-}BuO\cdot \qquad (5\text{-}3)$$

The *t*-butoxy radical then abstracts an allylic hydrogen from cyclohexene:

$$t\text{-}BuO\cdot + \text{cyclohexene} \longrightarrow t\text{-}BuOH + \text{cyclohexenyl radical} \qquad (5\text{-}4)$$

Products could result from either a radical process or an ionic one. In the radical process, the cyclohexenyl radical can be visualized as reacting with the complex formed in Reaction (5-3):

$$\text{cyclohexenyl radical} + (CH_3-CO_2\cdot Cu^{I}) \longrightarrow \text{3-cyclohexenyl-}O-\overset{O}{\overset{\|}{C}}-CH_3 + Cu^{I} \qquad (5\text{-}5)$$

However, the complex in (5-3) could also be written as Cu^{II} and a carboxylate anion:

$$CH_3-CO_2\cdot Cu^{I} \longrightarrow CH_3-CO_2^{-} + Cu^{II}$$

and carbonium ions can be envisioned as being formed by the oxidation of the cyclohexenyl radical:

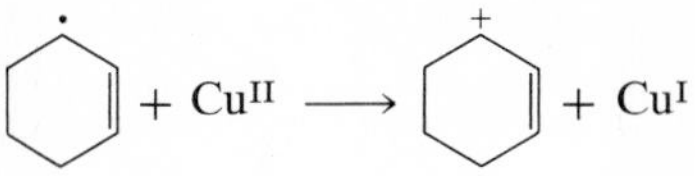

$$+ Cu^{II} \longrightarrow + Cu^{I}$$

Therefore, products could be produced by an ionic reaction which can be formulated as shown below.

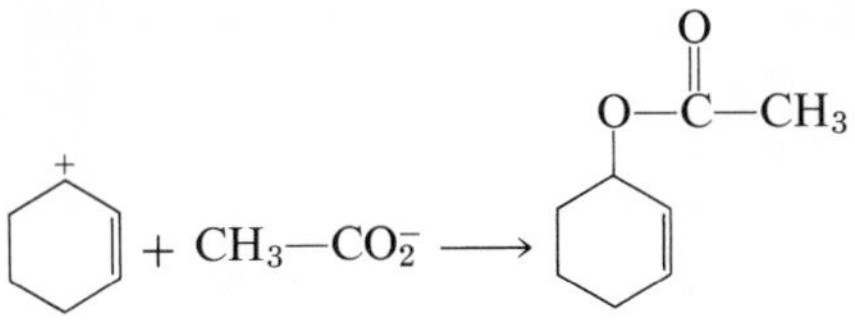

$$+ CH_3{-}CO_2^- \longrightarrow \quad O{-}\overset{\overset{O}{\|}}{C}{-}CH_3$$

Evidence that carbonium ions actually are intermediates in these reactions is derived from the occurrence of typical carbonium ion rearrangements;

Table 5-1

REACTIONS OF ACTIVE HYDROGEN DONORS WITH PERESTERS CATALYZED BY COPPER IONS

Active hydrogen compound	Peroxidic compound	Product	% Yield
$C_5H_{11}{-}CH_2{-}CH{=}CH_2$	$t\text{-BuO}{-}O{-}\overset{\overset{O}{\|}}{C}CH_3$	$C_5H_{11}{-}CH{=}CH{-}CH_2(O{-}CO{-}CH_3)$	12
		$C_5H_{11}{-}CH(O{-}CO{-}CH_3){-}CH{=}CH_2$	77
$\phi CH_2{-}O{-}\overset{\overset{O}{\|}}{C}{-}CH_3$	$t\text{-BuO}{-}O{-}\overset{\overset{O}{\|}}{C}\phi$	$\phi{-}CH(O{-}CO{-}\phi){-}O{-}\overset{\overset{O}{\|}}{C}{-}CH_3$	35
$\phi CH_2{-}O{-}\overset{\overset{O}{\|}}{C}{-}\phi$	$t\text{-BuO}{-}O{-}\overset{\overset{O}{\|}}{C}CH_3$	$\phi{-}CH(O{-}CO{-}\phi){-}O{-}\overset{\overset{O}{\|}}{C}{-}CH_3$	18
$\phi O{-}CH_2{-}CH{=}CH_2$	$t\text{-BuO}{-}O{-}\overset{\overset{O}{\|}}{C}{-}\phi$	$\phi O{-}CH(O{-}CO{-}\phi){-}CH{=}CH_2$	50
$\phi{-}CHO$	$t\text{-BuO}{-}O{-}\overset{\overset{O}{\|}}{C}{-}\phi$	$\phi{-}\overset{\overset{O}{\|}}{C}{-}O{-}\overset{\overset{O}{\|}}{C}{-}\phi$	70
	$t\text{-BuO}{-}O{-}\overset{\overset{O}{\|}}{C}{-}\phi$	$O{-}CO{-}\phi$	15
$C_3H_7{-}S{-}C_3H_7$	$t\text{-BuO}{-}O{-}\overset{\overset{O}{\|}}{C}{-}\phi$	$C_3H_7S{-}CH(O{-}CO{-}\phi){-}C_2H_5$	69

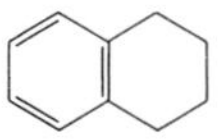

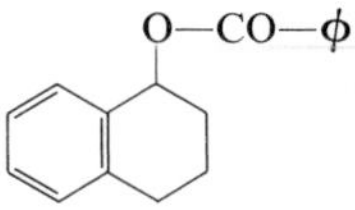

for example, 1,2-hydrogen and alkyl migrations accompany some of the copper catalyzed reactions. These rearrangements do not occur in radical intermediates.

Although the product forming reaction probably involves carbonium ion reactions, the hydrogen abstraction step (5-4) is a radical process. This is indicated by the fact that the relative reactivities of different substances in Reaction (5-4) is just that which would be predicted for a reaction in which a *t*-butoxy radical abstracts a hydrogen atom. For example, the relative reactivities of ethylbenzene: cumene: 2-hexene are 1.0: 0.4: 1.4 both in the copper-catalyzed reaction and in the reaction of these substrates with *t*-butoxy radicals generated from *t*-butyl hypochlorite. Examples of these copper catalyzed reactions are given in Table 5-1.

PROBLEM

1. Predict the products of the copper catalyzed reaction between ethylbenzene and *t*-butyl peracetate.

6 Hydrogen Abstraction Reactions

In Chap. 1 we discussed the three main types of radical reactions: initiations, propagation reactions, and terminations. In this and the following five chapters we now turn our attention to the more important types of propagation reactions that occur in radical chain reactions.

6.1 GENERAL FEATURES OF HYDROGEN ABSTRACTIONS

The most common reaction that radicals undergo is hydrogen abstraction. It can be generalized as is shown below, where AH is any hydrogen donor:

$$\mathrm{R}\cdot + \mathrm{AH} \longrightarrow \mathrm{RH} + \mathrm{A}\cdot$$

The energy required to break a bond is so large that normally the reaction cannot occur unassisted, and some bond-making occurs in the transition state:

$$\mathrm{R}\cdot + \mathrm{AH} \longrightarrow \underset{\text{transition state}}{[\mathrm{R}\cdots\cdot\mathrm{H}\cdots\cdot\mathrm{A}]} \longrightarrow \mathrm{RH} + \mathrm{A}\cdot$$

In this bimolecular process, the energy of formation of the new RH bond supplies part of the energy necessary to break the AH bond. Since the AH and RH bonds are both partially formed at the transition state, their strengths will influence the ease with which the hydrogen transfer occurs. Radicals which form strong bonds to hydrogen should abstract hydrogen particularly readily, and compounds which have weak AH bonds should be particularly good hydrogen donors. This expectation is confirmed in studies of hydrogen abstraction from aliphatic hydrocarbons, where hydrogen atoms are always abstracted at rates in the order primary $<$ secondary $<$ tertiary. This order is independent of the nature of the attacking radical and is attributed to the strengths of the C—H bonds being broken. Thus, tertiary C—H bonds are the weakest, and tertiary hydrogens are abstracted at the fastest rate.

Table 6-1

INFLUENCE OF THE STRENGTH OF THE BOND BEING FORMED ON THE ACTIVATION ENERGY FOR HYDROGEN ABSTRACTION FROM ETHANE

$$R\cdot + C_2H_6 \longrightarrow RH + \cdot C_2H_5$$

R·	Strength of the R—H bond (kcal/mole)	Activation energy for hydrogen abstraction reaction (kcal/mole)
F	136	0.2
Cl	103	1.0
H	103	9
CH_3	102	11
Br	87	14

The effect of the strength of the bond being formed in hydrogen transfer reactions is indicated by the data in Table 6-1. Atoms which form stronger bonds to hydrogen generally do abstract hydrogen at faster rates (i.e., with lower activation energies) as expected. Note, however, that Cl·, H·, and $\cdot CH_3$ all form bonds to hydrogen of nearly the same strength, yet they abstract hydrogen atoms from ethane with different activation energies. Clearly, other factors are involved, and the consideration of only the strength of the bond being formed is an oversimplification.

A relationship is sometimes observed between the *reactivity* of a radical and its *selectivity* in discriminating between different types of hydrogen atoms. For example, compare the products of the gas phase photolytic chlorination and bromination of isobutane:

$$CH_3-\overset{\displaystyle CH_3}{\underset{\displaystyle H}{\overset{|}{\underset{|}{C}}}}-CH_3 \xrightarrow{Cl_2} \underset{35\%}{CH_3-\overset{\displaystyle CH_3}{\underset{\displaystyle Cl}{\overset{|}{\underset{|}{C}}}}-CH_3} + \underset{65\%}{CH_3-\overset{\displaystyle CH_3}{\underset{\displaystyle H}{\overset{|}{\underset{|}{C}}}}-CH_2Cl}$$

$$CH_3-\overset{\displaystyle CH_3}{\underset{\displaystyle H}{\overset{|}{\underset{|}{C}}}}-CH_3 \xrightarrow{Br_2} \underset{100\%}{CH_3-\overset{\displaystyle CH_3}{\underset{\displaystyle Br}{\overset{|}{\underset{|}{C}}}}-CH_3}$$

Since the tertiary C—H bond in isobutane is weaker than the primary C—H bond, we would expect both chlorine and bromine atoms to preferentially abstract the tertiary hydrogen. Bromine atoms clearly do so, but the results indicate that more of the primary chloride is formed in the chlorination reaction. However, we must correct for the fact that there are nine primary hydrogens and only one tertiary hydrogen in isobutane and divide the relative yield of primary chloride by 9. Therefore, the relative reactivity of *one tertiary* to *one primary* hydrogen is 35 to 65/9, or 4.8 to 1. That is, chlorine atoms abstract a tertiary hydrogen 4.8 times faster than they abstract a single primary hydrogen. However, the selectivity is far less in chlorination than in bromination, since in bromination *only* the tertiary hydrogen is abstracted. Thus, chlorine atoms are *less* selective than are bromine atoms. The data in Table 6-1 show that chlorine atoms are much *more* reactive (i.e., they require far less activation energy to abstract a hydrogen atom). This inverse relationship between selectivity and reactivity is frequently observed in chemical reactions. Although this is not a thermodynamic relation, and need not always be obeyed, it is often found that very reactive species tend to be quite unselective in their reactions, whereas unreactive species tend to react quite selectively. Very reactive species usually undergo fast, exothermic reactions in which the bonds being altered are stretched only slightly in the transition state. Therefore, the nature and strength of these bonds have relatively little influence on the ease with which reaction occurs. On the other hand, the reactions of unreactive species usually involve considerable amounts of bond-making and bond-breaking in the transition state, and the strength of the bond being broken greatly influences the rate of the reaction.

The differences between selective, unreactive species and unselective, reactive species can be rationalized by the reaction coordinate diagram in Fig. 6-1. In this figure, two extreme chemical reactions are shown; a very exothermic and a very endothermic reaction. The starting material of the exothermic reaction has relatively high energy and requires a relatively small activation energy to react; it is a reactive species. Note that in this case the transition state lies near the starting material on the reaction coordinate; this implies that relatively little C—H bond-breaking has occurred at the transition state and that the exact nature of the C—H bond would have little influence on the rate of the process.

The endothermic reaction, on the other hand, involves a comparatively stable starting material and a high activation energy. Here, the transition state is closer to the products and considerable amounts of bond-breaking can be expected.

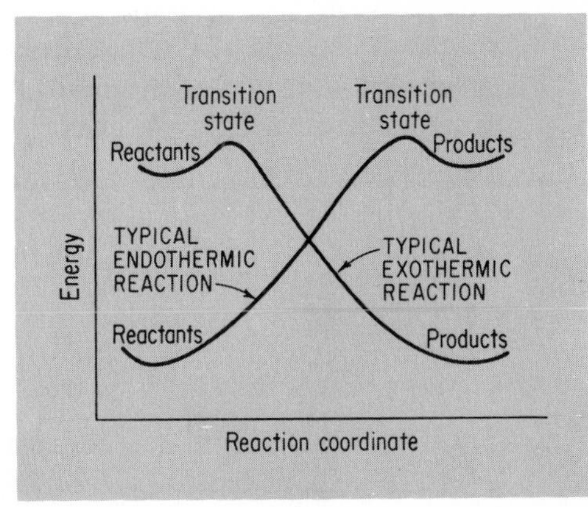

Fig. 6-1 Reaction coordinate diagram for a very exothermic and a very endothermic reaction.

In terms of these concepts, we can qualitatively picture the transition states for hydrogen abstraction by chlorine and bromine atoms as shown below:

$$\mathrm{Cl^{\bullet}} \qquad \mathrm{H \cdot\cdot R}$$

$$[\mathrm{Br^{\bullet}} \cdots\cdots \mathrm{H} \cdots \mathrm{R}]$$

transition states

More bond-making and bond-breaking has occurred at the transition state in the case of the relatively unreactive bromine atom, making its reactions more sensitive to the strength of the R—H bond being broken.

6.2 RELATIVE RATES

The rate of the reaction

$$R\cdot + AH \longrightarrow RH + A\cdot$$

is given by

$$\text{rate} = k(R\cdot)\,(AH)$$

The concentration of radicals usually is too small to be measured, even by methods as sensitive as epr (pp. 5–6). Consequently, ratios of rate constants for radical reactions are generally written so that the radical concentrations themselves are not required. This is best made clear by an example: methyl radicals can be generated in a mixed solvent consisting of the hydrogen donor AH and carbon tetrachloride. The reactions shown below then occur in competition:

$$CH_3\cdot + AH \xrightarrow{k_H} CH_4 + A\cdot$$

$$CH_3\cdot + CCl_4 \xrightarrow{k_{Cl}} CH_3Cl + \cdot CCl_3$$

The rate of formation of methane is given by

$$\frac{d(CH_4)}{dt} = k_H(CH_3\cdot)\,(AH)_0$$

and the rate of formation of chloromethane by

$$\frac{d(CH_3Cl)}{dt} = k_{Cl}(CH_3\cdot)\,(CCl_4)_0$$

The subscript zero in these equations indicates initial concentration, and we can assume that the concentrations of AH and CCl_4 are essentially unchanged during the reaction for the ratios of reactants used here. The ratio of these two rates is then

$$\frac{\dfrac{d(CH_4)}{dt}}{\dfrac{d(CH_3Cl)}{dt}} = \frac{d(CH_4)}{d(CH_3Cl)} = \frac{k_H(CH_3\cdot)(AH)_0}{k_{Cl}(CH_3\cdot)(CCl_4)_0}$$

or

$$\frac{d(CH_4)}{d(CH_3Cl)} = \frac{k_H(AH)_0}{k_{Cl}(CCl_4)_0}$$

Thus, if *ratios* of products are used, a rate expression can be obtained which is independent of the concentration of methyl radicals. Since the concentrations of both methane and chloromethane are zero at the beginning of the experiment, this equation can be integrated to give

$$\frac{[\text{yield of } CH_4 \text{ at time } t]}{[\text{yield of } CH_3Cl \text{ at time } t]} = \frac{k_H(AH)_0}{k_{Cl}(CCl_4)_0}$$

which can be rearranged to

$$\frac{k_H}{k_{Cl}} = \frac{[\text{yield of methane}]\ (CCl_4)_0}{[\text{yield of chloromethane}]\ (AH)_0}$$

In this way the rates of hydrogen abstraction from a series of hydrogen donors can be measured relative to the rate of chlorine abstraction from carbon tetrachloride.

The use of these equations can be clarified by a numerical example. If twice as much methane as chloromethane is formed from an equimolar mixture of AH and CCl_4, then $k_H/k_{Cl} = 2$, and methyl radicals react with AH twice as fast as with CCl_4. Similarly, if a mixture of BH and CCl_4 gives $k'_H/k_{Cl} = 4$, then we can conclude that methyl radicals abstract hydrogen twice as fast from BH as from AH.

The relative rate constants in Table 6-2 were obtained by these and similar techniques. The first column of rate constants gives the relative rates for abstraction of hydrogen atoms in the gas phase, and the second column applies to the liquid phase. Note that the order of reactivity of solvents toward methyl radicals is the same in either phase. Methyl radicals apparently interact very little with solvents and are unaffected by any kind of solvent effect. This is very frequently the case for radical reactions.

Table 6-3 gives data obtained in a similar manner for other radicals. Phenyl radicals can be generated by thermal decomposition of phenylazotriphenylmethane:

$$\phi\text{—N=N—C}\phi_3 \longrightarrow \phi\cdot + N_2 + \phi_3C\cdot$$

t-Butoxy radicals are conveniently produced either by the photolytic decomposition of *t*-butyl hypochlorite,

$$t\text{-BuOCl} \xrightarrow{\text{light}} t\text{-BuO}\cdot + Cl\cdot$$

or by thermolysis of *t*-butyl peroxide:

$$t\text{-BuO—OBu-}t \longrightarrow 2t\text{-BuO}\cdot$$

Table 6-2

RELATIVE RATES OF HYDROGEN ABSTRACTION BY METHYL RADICALS

$$CH_3\cdot + AH \xrightarrow{k_H} CH_4 + A\cdot$$

AH	Rel. k_H gas phase, 100°C	Rel. k_H solution, 100°C	Ratio $\frac{k_{gas}}{k_{solution}}$
Benzene	0.09	0.1	0.9
Acetone	1.0	1.0	1.0
Toluene	1.9	1.9	1.0
1-Octene	7.7	8.0	0.95

Table 6-3

RELATIVE REACTIVITIES (PER HYDROGEN) OF HYDROGEN DONORS TOWARD SEVERAL RADICALS IN THE LIQUID PHASE†

Hydrogen donor	Radical				
	Methyl 65°C	Phenyl 60°C	*t*-Butoxy 40°C	Chlorine atoms 40°C	Bromine atoms 40°C
Cyclohexane	—	1.0	1.5	2.0	0.004
Toluene	(1)	(1)	(1)	(1)	(1)
Ethylbenzene	4.1	4.6	3.2	2.5	17.2
Isopropylbenzene	12.9	9.7	6.9	5.5	37.0
Acetone	0.30	0.17	—	—	—

†All reactivities are calculated per hydrogen atom, and only benzylic hydrogens are considered in the alkylbenzene compounds. Values in parentheses are assumed as standard values.

Chlorine and bromine atoms are produced by photolytic decomposition of the molecular halogens:

$$Cl_2 \xrightarrow{\text{light}} 2Cl\cdot$$

$$Br_2 \xrightarrow{\text{light}} 2Br\cdot$$

The data in Table 6-3 show that all the radicals abstract benzylic hydrogen atoms in the usual order: primary < secondary < tertiary. The selectivity of these radicals toward benzylic hydrogens increases in the order: $Cl\cdot < t\text{-BuO}\cdot < \phi\cdot < CH_3\cdot < Br\cdot$. Bromine atoms are considerably more selective than any of the other radicals.

6.3 POLAR EFFECTS

A naive picture of radicals might assume that they are not subject to the same kinds of polar influences that affect the reactions of charged species and would not be influenced by the electronic nature of the reactants. This is very often the case, but sometimes radical reactions show pronounced effects due to polar influences. For example, the data below give the relative rates at which a chlorine atom abstracts a hydrogen from the various positions in butane and 1-fluorobutane:

CH_3—	CH_2—	CH_2—	CH_3	CH_2F—	CH_2—	CH_2—	CH_3
1.0	3.7	3.7	1.0	0.9	1.7	3.7	1.0

relative rates

The preference of chlorine atoms for secondary hydrogens relative to primary can be seen in the data for butane. This selectivity is due to the fact that secondary C—H bonds are weaker than primary. In 1-fluorobutane, this normal preference is seen in the rates of attack on the hydrogens farthest from the fluorine substituent. However, the *decrease* in rate of attack on the hydrogens nearest the fluorine must be due to a *repulsion of the attacking electronegative chlorine atom caused by electron withdrawal by the electronegative fluorine substituent.*

Table 6-4

RELATIVE SELECTIVITY OF Cl· AND ·CH_3 TOWARD THE HYDROGENS IN PROPIONIC ACID

Relative selectivity	CH_3—	CH_2—CO_2H
CH_3·	1	7.8
Cl·	30	1

The data in Table 6-4 compare the reactivity of methyl radicals and chlorine atoms toward the hydrogens in propionic acid. Methyl radicals attack an α-hydrogen 7.8-fold *faster* than a β-hydrogen, whereas chlorine atoms attack an α-hydrogen 30 times *slower* than a β-hydrogen. These facts are most easily explained in terms of a polar effect due to the electron-withdrawing carboxylic acid group. The relatively electropositive methyl radicals prefer to attack those hydrogens closest to the electronegative carboxyl group. The reverse is true for the relatively electronegative chlorine atoms. In analogy with the terminology used in ionic reactions, methyl radicals can be thought of as relatively nucleophilic, whereas chlorine atoms are relatively electrophilic radicals.

Polar effects in radical reactions can be explained and predicted by writing resonance structures that involve charge separation for the transition states of the reactions. For example, attack of the electronegative chlorine atom on the hydrocarbon RH can be pictured as below:

$$\mathrm{Cl}\cdot + \mathrm{RH} \longrightarrow [\dot{\mathrm{Cl}}\ \mathrm{H{:}R} \longleftrightarrow \mathrm{Cl{:}^-}\ \dot{\mathrm{H}}\ {}^+\mathrm{R}] \longrightarrow \mathrm{HCl} + \mathrm{R}\cdot$$

transition state

The charge-separated resonance structure shown is that in which negative charge is localized on the chlorine atom since it is more electronegative than either the hydrogen atom or the alkyl radical R. This charge-separated structure leads to the prediction that electron-supplying groups in R should increase the rate of hydrogen abstraction by chlorine atoms, and electron-withdrawing groups should decrease the rate of abstraction. This is in agreement with the data in Table 6-4 in which the electron-withdrawing carboxy group slows hydrogen abstraction at adjacent carbon atoms. The transition state for the reactions of chlorine atoms with propionic acid is shown below:

$$\left[\begin{array}{c} \mathrm{H} \\ \mathrm{CH_3{-}\underset{|}{\overset{|}{C}}{-}CO_2H} \\ \mathrm{H} \\ \mathrm{Cl}\cdot \end{array} \longleftrightarrow \begin{array}{c} \mathrm{H} \\ \mathrm{CH_3{-}\overset{|}{C}{}^{+}{-}CO_2H} \\ \mathrm{H}\cdot \\ \mathrm{Cl{:}^-} \end{array}\right]$$

transition state

The electron-withdrawing inductive effect of the carboxy group destabilizes the charge-separated resonance structure shown on the right.

The rate of reaction of substituted toluenes with chlorine atoms is another example of these phenomena. As shown below, the electron-donating *p*-phenoxy group increases the rate, whereas the electron-withdrawing *p*-nitro group decreases it:

$$Cl\cdot + CH_3-C_6H_4-X \longrightarrow HCl + \cdot CH_2-C_6H_4-X$$

X	Relative rate
ϕO	2.5
H	1.0
NO_2	0.3

The rate enhancing effect of the *p*-phenoxy group can be explained by writing charge-separated resonance structures for the transition state as shown below:

$$\left[\dot{Cl}\ H:CH_2-C_6H_4-O\phi \longleftrightarrow Cl:^-\ \dot{H}^+CH_2-C_6H_4-O\phi \longleftrightarrow Cl:^-\ \dot{H}\ CH_2=C_6H_4=\overset{+}{O}\phi\right]$$

transition state

6.4 SOLVENT EFFECTS

Solvent effects usually are so much smaller in radical reactions than in ionic reactions that the lack of pronounced solvent effect is used as a diagnostic tool for identifying radical processes. For example, alkyl peroxides dissociate at the same rate in the gas phase as in solutions of benzene, cumene, amines, and other solvents:

$$ROOR \longrightarrow \underset{\text{transition state}}{[RO\cdots\cdot OR]} \longrightarrow 2RO\cdot$$

Apparently there is very little charge separation in the transition state, and solvation by polar solvent molecules plays little role in aiding this dissociation. In contrast, the dissociation of alkyl halides into ions occurs as much as 10^{100} times faster in a polar solvent such as water than in the gas phase:

$$R-Cl \longrightarrow \underset{\text{transition state}}{\left[\overset{\delta+}{R}\cdots\cdot\overset{\delta-}{Cl}\right]} \longrightarrow R^+ + Cl^-$$

In these ionic reactions an appreciable charge separation has developed at the transition state, and polar solvents stabilize this separation and increase the reaction rate.

Table 6-5

THE PRODUCT DISTRIBUTION IN THE CHLORINATION OF 2,3-DIMETHYLBUTANE

$$CH_3-\underset{H}{\overset{CH_3}{C}}-\underset{H}{\overset{CH_3}{C}}-CH_3 \xrightarrow[h\nu]{Cl_2} Cl-CH_2-\underset{H}{\overset{CH_3}{C}}-\underset{H}{\overset{CH_3}{C}}-CH_3 + CH_3-\underset{Cl}{\overset{CH_3}{C}}-\underset{H}{\overset{CH_3}{C}}-CH_3$$

I II

Solvent	% I	% II
Carbon tetrachloride	60	40
Benzene	10	90
Carbon disulfide	5	95

In some radical reactions, however, the effects of changing solvents are very significant. One notable example is the chlorination of 2,3-dimethylbutane, where the product distribution is completely altered by a change in solvent (Table 6-5). Tertiary C—H bonds are weaker than primary, and therefore should be broken more easily. However, there are 12 primary but only two tertiary hydrogens in 2,3-dimethylbutane. In carbon tetrachloride as solvent, the chlorine atom is very reactive and shows little selectivity, and the larger number of primary hydrogens leads to a larger amount of primary alkyl chloride being formed. However, benzene and carbon disulfide complex with the chlorine atom and stabilize it, and this stabilized chlorine atom is more selective in its reactions than the free chlorine atom. Table 6-5 shows that in these two solvents the main product is the tertiary chloride. We can picture the reaction of the complexed and stabilized chlorine atom in carbon disulfide as shown below:

$$Cl\cdot + CS_2 \rightleftharpoons (CS_2\cdot Cl)$$

$$(CS_2\cdot Cl) + RH \longrightarrow HCl + R\cdot + CS_2$$

Notice that the solvent effect reflected in the data of Table 6-5 is *not* due to changes in the dielectric constants of the solvents, but is due rather to a specific interaction between the solvent and the radicals. The rates of most radical reactions are independent of the dielectric constant of the medium.

PROBLEMS

1. Give an explanation for the fact that hydrogen atoms in saturated hydrocarbons are always abstracted at a rate primary $<$ secondary $<$ tertiary regardless of the nature of the attacking radical.

2. From the data in Table 6-1, would you predict that fluorination of organic compounds would be very selective? Explain why very reactive species tend to be unselective.

3. Why is the maximum difference in the relative reactivities in Table 6-3 so much larger for bromination than for chlorination?

4. Comment on the fact that the product composition in the chlorination of 2,3-dimethylbutane is very dependent on the chemical nature of the solvent but not on its dielectric constant.

5. When *t*-butyl peroxide is allowed to decompose in a hydrocarbon RH, the products include *t*-butyl alcohol, acetone, methane, and products from termination reactions of R· radicals. Derive an equation which gives the ratio of the rate constants for the two reactions shown below. Your expression should not involve the concentration of radicals. How could this expression be used to measure the relative reactivities of a series of hydrogen donors?

$$t\text{-BuO}\cdot \xrightarrow{k} CH_3\text{—CO—}CH_3 + \cdot CH_3$$

$$t\text{-BuO}\cdot + RH \xrightarrow{k_H} t\text{-BuOH} + R\cdot$$

6. Explain why a *p*-phenoxy group increases and a *p*-nitro group decreases the rate of chlorination of toluene. Give a full explanation which includes resonance structures for the transition states of both reactions.

7. In contrast to the results discussed for chlorine atoms, neither methyl radicals nor bromine atoms show solvent effects; these two radicals react with virtually the same relative rates in the gas phase, in inert solvents, and in benzene. Explain.

SUGGESTED FURTHER READINGS

De La Mare, H. E., and Vaughan, W. E., "Detection and Reactions of Alkyl Free Radicals in the Gas Phase," *J. Chem. Ed.,* **34**(1957), 10.

Gritter, R. J., "Free Radical Chemistry in Solution," *J. Chem. Ed.,* **35**(1958), 475.

The following books are monographs written for advanced students, but may be consulted for a more detailed treatment of radical reactions:

Pryor, William A., *Free Radicals.* New York: McGraw-Hill Book Company, 1966.

Trotman-Dickenson, A. F., *Free Radicals: An Introduction.* ("Methuen's Monographs.") New York: John Wiley & Sons, Inc., 1959.

Walling, Cheves, *Free Radicals in Solution.* New York: John Wiley & Sons, Inc., 1957.

7 Halogenation

As was discussed in Chap. 1, halogenation involves the sequence of chain propagating steps shown below:

$$X\cdot + RH \longrightarrow R\cdot + HX$$

$$R\cdot + X_2 \longrightarrow RX + X\cdot$$

We have already seen several examples of these processes, and in this chapter we shall consider the details more fully.

7.1 FLUORINATION

Fluorine reacts with organic molecules with considerable violence, and organic fluorides usually are produced by indirect methods. However, fluorination can be studied in the vapor phase by diluting the fluorine with nitrogen or another gas that is inert. The reactions are very fast and exothermic, and the usual products include all possible polyfluoro compounds as well as CF_4. Both steps in the chain sequence are extremely exothermic. For example, for methane the heats of reaction are:

	ΔH (kcal/mole)
$F\cdot + CH_4 \longrightarrow HF + \cdot CH_3$	-32
$CH_3\cdot + F_2 \longrightarrow CH_3F + F\cdot$	-70

Fluorination occurs in the dark even at $-80°C$. Simple homolysis of fluorine, as shown below, is too endothermic a reaction to be an initiation step at low temperatures:

$$F_2 \longrightarrow 2F\cdot \qquad \Delta H = 37 \text{ kcal/mole}$$

Therefore, bimolecular processes have been suggested for the initiation step. For example, a molecule-induced homolysis involving fluorine and an alkane can be postulated; this is shown below for the case of methane:

$$F_2 + CH_4 \longrightarrow HF + F\cdot + \cdot CH_3$$

This reaction would have a heat of reaction of 5 kcal/mole:

$$\Delta H = D(\text{F—F}) + D(\text{CH}_3\text{—H}) - D(\text{H—F}) = 37 + 102 - 134 = 5$$

The reaction of fluorine with olefins can be formulated as producing radicals in a reaction that would be slightly exothermic. For example, the reaction with ethene can be calculated to have a heat of reaction of about −2 kcal/mole:

$$CH_2{=}CH_2 + F_2 \longrightarrow FCH_2{-}\dot{C}H_2 + F\cdot \qquad \Delta H = -2 \text{ kcal/mole}$$

These calculations led to the prediction that small amounts of fluorine should act as an initiator for halogenation by chlorine and bromine, and this has been verified.

7.2 CHLORINATION

Radical chlorination is of enormous utility and has been the subject of literally hundreds of investigations. When mixtures of hydrocarbons and chlorine are heated to 200° C, or are irradiated with light of wave length less than 4875 Å, a chain reaction occurs:

Reaction	ΔH (kcal/mole)
$Cl_2 \longrightarrow 2Cl\cdot$	58
$Cl\cdot + CH_4 \longrightarrow HCl + \cdot CH_3$	−1
$CH_3\cdot + Cl_2 \longrightarrow CH_3Cl + Cl\cdot$	−23

From the bond strengths, $D(CH_3{-}Cl) = 81$, $D(CH_3{-}H) = 102$, $D(H{-}Cl) = 103$, and $D(Cl{-}Cl) = 58$, the heats of the reactions can be calculated as shown above. The chlorine atom is much less reactive than is the fluorine, and only one of the steps in the chain is significantly exothermic. However, neither reaction has an appreciable activation energy, and both would be expected to occur very rapidly.

A considerable amount of information is known about the nature of the products which are formed from chlorination of organic substances:

1. Carbon skeleton rearrangements do not occur during chlorination.
2. Every possible monochloride is formed.
3. Hydrogen atoms are substituted at rates in the order tertiary > secondary > primary.
4. At increasing temperatures these relative rates approach 1:1:1.
5. Liquid phase chlorination gives higher rates than vapor phase at any given temperature.
6. Moisture, surfaces, and light have no effect on these ratios.

Table 7-1 gives some relative reactivities obtained from the analysis of the products of chlorination of various substrates in the gas phase. The data show that electronegative substituents slow the chlorination of nearby carbon atoms. For example, compare the first two lines in the table: A chlorine substituent does not alter the relative reactivity of the 3rd and 4th carbons. However, the electron withdrawing chlorine substituent greatly decreases the rate of attack by an electrophilic chlorine atom at the 1st and 2nd carbon atoms (also see pp. 56–57).

Chlorinations can be effected in the liquid as well as the gas phase, and in the condensed phase, molecule-induced homolyses become important (discussion on pp. 31–33). For example, in cyclohexene at 25 °C in the dark, chlorine rapidly reacts to give the three products shown below:

Table 7-1

SELECTIVITY OF CHLORINATIONS IN THE GAS PHASE†

C—	C—	C—	C
1	3.6	3.6	1
C—	C—	C—	CH_2Cl
1	3.7	2.1	0.8
C—	C—	C—	CH_2F
1	3.7	1.7	0.9
C—	C—	C—	C(=O)—Cl
1	3	0.2	
C—	C—	C—	CO_2CH_3
1	3	0	

† These selectivities are per hydrogen atom, and normalized so that the terminal atoms in each molecule are given unit activity.

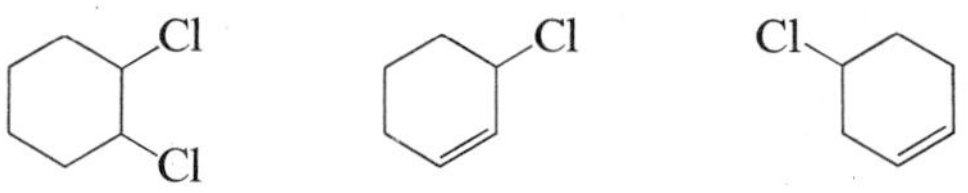

I II III

If the cyclohexene is diluted with a non-olefinic solvent, or if a radical inhibitor such as oxygen is present, product III is not formed. The most likely explanation of these facts is that products I, II, and III are produced by radical chlorination of cyclohexene, and products I and II are produced in a concurrent, ionic process. Therefore, the presence of an inhibitor eliminates product III. The mechanism of the ionic reactions which give I and II are ordinary electrophilic processes as shown below:

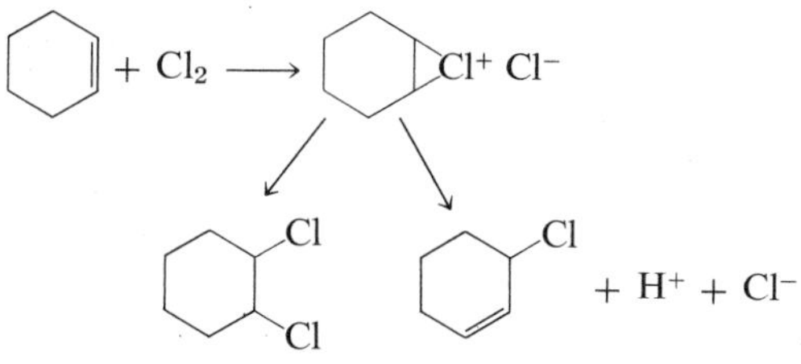

$+ Cl_2 \longrightarrow$ Cl^+ Cl^-

I II $+ H^+ + Cl^-$

However, product III could not be formed from any known ionic reaction, but would be expected to be produced in a radical chlorination. This radical process must be a molecule-induced homolysis since the homolysis of chlorine at 25 °C would occur much too slowly to explain the rate of appearance of III. Therefore, the interaction of cyclohexene and chlorine pro-

Table 7-2

RELATIVE REACTIVITIES OF CARBON-HYDROGEN BONDS TOWARD CHLORINE ATOMS AT 40°C†

RH	Solvent	Relative reactivity (per hydrogen atom)
Methane	Vapor	0.0044
Ethane	Vapor	1.05
Propane,		
primary H	Vapor	1.25
secondary H	Vapor	4.42
Butane,		
primary H	Vapor	1.47
secondary H	Vapor	5.15
Isobutane,		
primary H	Vapor	1.29
tertiary H	Vapor	6.25
2,3-Dimethylbutane,		
primary H	Reactants	1.0
tertiary H	Reactants	3.9
Cyclohexane	Cyclohexane	2.7
Toluene	Cyclohexane	1.4
Ethylbenzene,		
α-H	Cyclohexane	3.5
β-H	Cyclohexane	1.8
Isopropylbenzene,		
α-H	Cyclohexane	7.8
β-H	Cyclohexane	2.2
t-Butylbenzene	CCl_4	0.63
Diphenylmethane	Cyclohexane	2.7
Triphenylmethane	Nitrobenzene	10

† Liquid phase reactivities have been extrapolated to infinite dilution.

duces radicals *at a rapid rate at 25° C in the dark.* The radical nature of the process is demonstrated by the fact that if cyclohexane is present it also becomes chlorinated. Since cyclohexane would be expected to be inert to any ionic chlorination process, this is powerful evidence that chlorine atoms must be produced in an interaction between chlorine and cyclohexene, and these relatively unselective chlorine atoms then abstract hydrogen from any hydrogen donor which is present. (The mechanism for molecule-induced homolysis involving chlorine and olefins is discussed on pp. 33–34.)

Table 7-2 combines both gas and liquid phase rate data on chlorinations. Note that the order of hydrogen atom reactivities is always primary < secondary < tertiary. Thus, the series CH_4, ϕ—CH_3, ϕ_2CH_2, ϕ_3CH has the relative reactivities 1: 320: 615: 2300, and the series CH_4, CH_3—CH_3, $(CH_3)_2CH_2$, $(CH_3)_3CH$ has the relative reactivities 1: 240: 1000: 1400. Also note that toluene and ethane have about the same reactivity. Chlorine atoms are highly reactive, and very little bond breaking has occurred in the transition state; since relatively little electron density is localized at the α-carbon, the ability of the phenyl group to delocalize an odd electron is not utilized.

7.3 BROMINATION

The bromine atom is considerably more stable than is the chlorine atom, and the second step in the chain sequence for bromination is endothermic:

	ΔH (kcal/mole)
$CH_3\cdot + Br_2 \longrightarrow CH_3{-}Br + Br\cdot$	-21
$Br\cdot + CH_4 \longrightarrow HBr + \cdot CH_3$	15

Brominations, therefore, require elevated temperatures for any but the most activated C—H bonds.

Table 7-3 combines rate data for bromination in both liquid and gas phases. Bromine atoms are more selective than are chlorine atoms, and the total range of relative rates from methane to triphenylmethane is over 10^9 for bromination, whereas for chlorination it is only 10^3.

7.4 IODINATION

The heats of reaction for the two steps in the iodination of methane are:

	ΔH (kcal/mole)
$I_2 + \cdot CH_3 \longrightarrow CH_3I + I\cdot$	-18
$I\cdot + CH_4 \longrightarrow HI + \cdot CH_3$	$+33$

Table 7-3

RELATIVE REACTIVITIES OF CARBON-HYDROGEN BONDS TOWARD BROMINE ATOMS AT 40°C

RH	Phase	Relative reactivity (per hydrogen atom)
Methane	Vapor	0.0007
Ethane	Vapor	1.0
Propane, secondary H	Vapor	220.
Isobutane, tertiary H	Vapor	19×10^3
Toluene, α-H	CCl_4	64×10^3
Ethylbenzene, α-H	CCl_4	1×10^6
Isopropylbenzene, α-H	CCl_4	2.3×10^6
Diphenylmethane, α-H	CCl_4	0.6×10^6
Triphenylmethane, α-H	CCl_4	1.1×10^6

Hydrogen abstraction by iodine atoms is appreciably endothermic, and iodine atoms do not react with alkanes at moderate temperatures. However, iodine atoms do react with alkyl iodides to abstract iodine:

$$\text{I}\cdot + \text{RI} \longrightarrow \text{I}_2 + \text{R}\cdot$$

7.5 HALOGENATION BY HYPOHALITES

Hypohalites frequently are used as halogenation agents. For example, *t*-butyl hypochlorite reacts with hydrocarbons to yield alkyl chlorides. The chain mechanism for this reaction is

$$t\text{-BuO}\cdot + \text{RH} \longrightarrow t\text{-BuOH} + \text{R}\cdot$$
$$\text{R}\cdot + t\text{-BuOCl} \longrightarrow \text{RCl} + t\text{-BuO}\cdot$$

Relative reactivities of various hydrocarbons to *t*-butyl hypochlorite have been measured, and they parallel the reactivity of these compounds toward *t*-butyl peroxide, indicating that the species which abstracts a hydrogen is the *t*-butoxy radical in both cases.

In some compounds, *t*-butyl hypochlorite leads to different products than does molecular chlorine. For example, cyclopropane yields chlorocyclopropane with *t*-butyl hypochlorite:

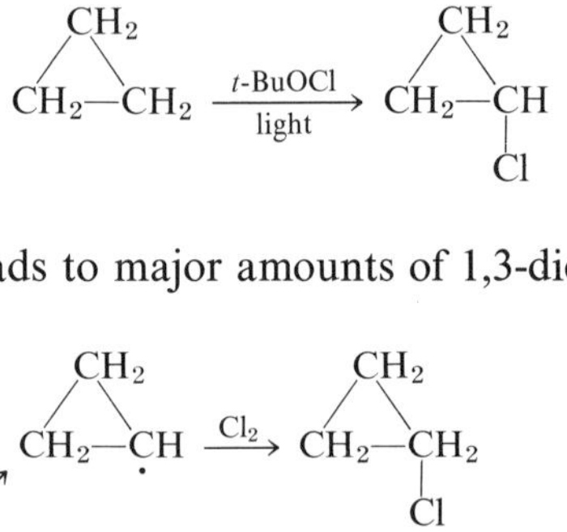

$$\text{cyclo-}(\text{CH}_2\text{—CH}_2\text{—CH}_2) \xrightarrow[\text{light}]{t\text{-BuOCl}} \text{cyclo-}(\text{CH}_2\text{—CH}_2\text{—CHCl})$$

However, chlorine leads to major amounts of 1,3-dichloropropane:

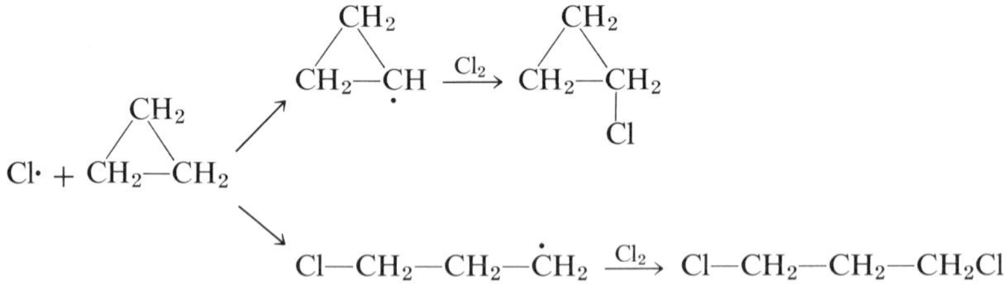

$$\text{Cl}\cdot + \text{cyclo-}(\text{CH}_2\text{—CH}_2\text{—CH}_2) \nearrow \text{cyclo-}(\text{CH}_2\text{—CH}_2\text{—}\dot{\text{C}}\text{H}) \xrightarrow{\text{Cl}_2} \text{cyclo-}(\text{CH}_2\text{—CH}_2\text{—CHCl})$$

$$\searrow \text{Cl—CH}_2\text{—CH}_2\text{—}\dot{\text{C}}\text{H}_2 \xrightarrow{\text{Cl}_2} \text{Cl—CH}_2\text{—CH}_2\text{—CH}_2\text{Cl}$$

The lower of these two reactions is interesting in that it could be an example of a radical displacement reaction on a carbon atom:

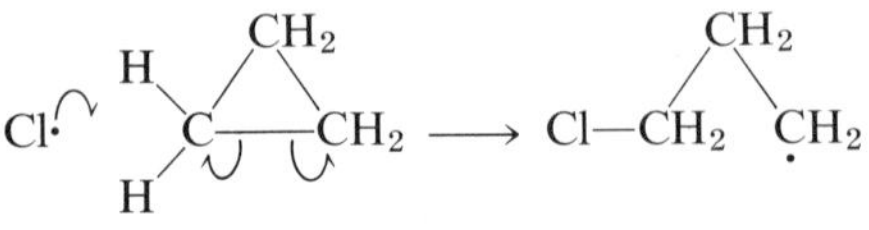

$$\text{Cl}\cdot \curvearrowright \text{cyclo-}(\text{H}_2\text{C—CH}_2\text{—CH}_2) \longrightarrow \text{Cl—CH}_2\text{—CH}_2\text{—}\dot{\text{C}}\text{H}_2$$

Hypohalite compounds provide a convenient route to alkoxy radicals. For example, alkoxy radicals can be generated as below:

$$\text{ROH} \xrightarrow{\text{HOCl}} \text{ROCl} \xrightarrow{\text{light}} \text{RO}\cdot + \text{Cl}\cdot$$

Hypohalites from tertiary alcohols have been studied most thoroughly; they react by hydrogen abstraction or decompose by β-scission:

$$\text{R}-\underset{\text{CH}_3}{\overset{\text{CH}_3}{\text{C}}}-\text{OCl} \xrightarrow[(-\text{Cl}\cdot)]{\text{light}} \text{R}-\underset{\text{CH}_3}{\overset{\text{CH}_3}{\text{C}}}-\text{O}\cdot + \text{AH} \xrightarrow{k_a} \text{R}-\underset{\text{CH}_3}{\overset{\text{CH}_3}{\text{C}}}-\text{OH} + \text{A}\cdot$$

$$\xrightarrow{k_d} \text{R}\cdot + \text{CH}_3-\overset{\text{O}}{\overset{\|}{\text{C}}}-\text{CH}_3$$

where k_a is the rate constant for hydrogen abstraction and k_d that for decomposition. In unsymmetrical alkoxy radicals, more than one alkyl group can be eliminated. Normally, the products formed in largest yield are those which result from elimination of the most stable radical (p. 4 contains typical data). It has been found that alkyl groups are eliminated as a free radical from alkoxy radicals in the order: *t*-butyl > isopropyl > benzyl ≅ ethyl > chloromethyl > methyl.

7.6 HALOGENATION BY N-BROMOSUCCINIMIDE

N-Bromosuccinimide (NBS) brominates organic compounds in a reaction that can be initiated by light and by benzoyl peroxide or other typical radical sources. The reaction was recognized to be a radical chain process in 1944, and has been studied extensively as a useful synthetic tool. The special feature of NBS that makes it particularly useful is that it is extremely selective; allylic and benzylic bromination can be effected in excellent yield. The examples below illustrate this:

$$\text{cyclohexene} \xrightarrow[\text{ether, 25°C}]{\text{NBS}} \text{3-bromocyclohexene (Br)}$$

50–80%

$$\text{CH}_2{=}\text{CH}-\text{CH}_3 \xrightarrow{\text{NBS}} \text{CH}_2{=}\text{CH}-\text{CH}_2\text{Br}$$

29%

$$\phi\text{CH}{=}\text{CH}-\text{CH}_3 \xrightarrow{\text{NBS}} \phi\text{CH}{=}\text{CH}-\text{CH}_2\text{Br}$$

75%

$$\phi\text{CH}_3 \xrightarrow{\text{NBS}} \phi\text{CH}_2\text{Br}$$

At first it was thought that these reactions involved the succinimidyl radical as a halogen carrier, much as the *t*-butoxy radical is involved in the reactions of *t*-butyl hypochlorite. However, recent studies have proved this to be incorrect, and the correct mechanism is shown below:

$$Br\cdot + RH \longrightarrow HBr + R\cdot$$

$$R\cdot + Br_2 \longrightarrow R{-}Br + Br\cdot$$

$$HBr + \text{(succinimide)N{-}Br} \longrightarrow Br_2 + \text{(succinimide)N{-}H}$$

In this mechanism, low concentrations of bromine function as the active brominating agent; NBS merely acts as a bromine reservoir. Note that allylic bromination occurs in preference to addition to the double bond. This competition is illustrated below for the case of cyclohexene:

$$Br\cdot + \text{cyclohexene} \xrightarrow[\text{abstraction by Br}\cdot]{\text{hydrogen}} \text{cyclohexenyl radical} \xrightarrow{Br_2} \text{3-bromocyclohexene} + Br\cdot$$

$$Br\cdot + \text{cyclohexene} \underset{}{\overset{\text{addition}}{\rightleftharpoons}} \text{2-bromocyclohexyl radical} \xrightarrow{Br_2} \text{1,2-dibromocyclohexane} + Br\cdot$$

Since the addition of bromine atoms to the double bond is reversible, a low bromine concentration favors the hydrogen abstraction step. This explanation is supported by the fact that bromination by low concentrations of molecular bromine also favors allylic bromination. Actually, the hydrogen abstraction step shown in the above scheme is also reversible

$$Br\cdot + RH \rightleftharpoons R\cdot + HBr$$

However, NBS reacts with hydrogen bromide, keeps its concentration low, and minimizes reversal of the above reaction. Thus, NBS is a convenient reagent for maintaining a low concentration of bromine at the expense of hydrogen bromide.

In the competitive bromination of substituted toluenes, it is found that molecular bromine and NBS show identical relative reactivities. In fact, N-bromotetrafluorosuccinimide, N-bromotetramethylsuccinimide, NBS, and bromine all have identical reactivities, and N-bromoacetamide and various N-bromohydantoins have very similar reactivities. This makes it very probable that the active species is molecular bromine in all of these cases.

Table 7-4 illustrates the greater selectivity of NBS as a halogenating agent when compared with chlorine or *t*-butyl hypochlorite. The ratio of

Table 7-4

RELATIVE REACTIVITIES OF HYDROCARBONS TOWARD THREE HALOGENATING REAGENTS

Hydrocarbons	Chlorine 40°C	*t*-Butyl hypochlorite 40°C	NBS 80°C
Cyclohexene	—	36	129
Toluene	(1)	(1)	(1)
Ethylbenzene	—	3.2	24
Isopropylbenzene	4.0	6.8	50
Cyclohexane	2.3	1.5	0.003
2,3-Dimethylbutane	3.4	4.2	0.1

rates of cyclohexene to cyclohexane is 4×10^4 for NBS, but only 24 for *t*-butyl hypochlorite. These data indicate that NBS is the preferred reagent for selective halogenation of complex molecules.

PROBLEMS

1. Explain why long chains are easily obtained in chlorinations and less easily in brominations. Why does iodination not normally occur by a radical chain reaction?

2. Explain why methyl butanoate is chlorinated chiefly at the β-carbon atom (Table 7-1).

3. Why is the yield of 4-chlorocyclohexene in the reaction of cyclohexene and chlorine less if the cyclohexene is diluted with a non-olefinic solvent?

4. Why is the difference in reactivities so much greater in Table 7-3 than in Table 7-2?

5. Chlorine reacts with cyclohexane slightly faster than with toluene, whereas bromine reacts with toluene faster than with cyclohexane (see p. 56). Explain these facts. (Hint: a phenyl group has an electron-withdrawing inductive effect.)

6. Refer to the data on p. 52 which compare the relative selectivity in chlorination and bromination of isobutane, and using the data in Table 7-3, estimate the reactivity difference between primary and tertiary hydrogens in bromination of isobutane. What percent of $BrCH_2—CH(CH_3)_2$ would be expected in the monobromination product? Explain why bromination is so much more selective than chlorination.

7. The data in Table 7-2 for the reactivity of aromatic species such as toluene have been extrapolated to infinite dilution of the toluene in a non-olefinic solvent such as carbon tetrachloride. Why is this necessary?

8 Addition

A wide range of molecules add to the C—C double bond in radical chain processes; addends include hydrogen bromide, the halogens, hydrogen sulfide, thiols, various halomethanes such as carbon tetrachloride, alcohols, aldehydes and many others. Depending on the factors which we will discuss below, the product of the addition of AB to the olefin $\rangle C{=}C\langle$ can either be the simple one-to-one adduct

$$A-\overset{|}{\underset{|}{C}}-\overset{|}{\underset{|}{C}}-B$$

or products called telomers, in which one molecule of AB combines with many molecules of the olefin:

$$A\left(\overset{|}{\underset{|}{C}}-\overset{|}{\underset{|}{C}}\right)_n B$$

$$n = 2 \text{ to about } 100$$

or materials, which are essentially polymerization products of the olefin with one part of the addend on each end:

$$A\left(\overset{|}{\underset{|}{C}}-\overset{|}{\underset{|}{C}}\right)_n B$$

$$n > \text{about } 100$$

As we shall see, these are all chain processes, and the number of moles of products produced per mole of initiating radicals, called the chain length, is often as large as 10^6.

8.1 THE GENERALIZED MECHANISM OF THE REACTION

Although radical addition reactions can yield diverse products, the mechanisms may be described in terms of the reactions summarized below:

$$AB \xrightarrow[\text{or light}]{\text{initiators}} B\cdot$$

Step 1:

$$\mathrm{B\cdot + \; >C{=}C< \;\longrightarrow\; B{-}\overset{|}{\underset{|}{C}}{-}\overset{|}{\underset{|}{C}}\cdot}$$

I

Step 2:

$$\mathrm{B{-}\overset{|}{\underset{|}{C}}{-}\overset{|}{\underset{|}{C}}\cdot + AB \;\longrightarrow\; B{-}\overset{|}{\underset{|}{C}}{-}\overset{|}{\underset{|}{C}}{-}A + B\cdot}$$

I II

Step 3:

$$\mathrm{B{-}\overset{|}{\underset{|}{C}}{-}\overset{|}{\underset{|}{C}}\cdot + \; >C{=}C< \;\longrightarrow\; B{+}\left(\overset{|}{\underset{|}{C}}{-}\overset{|}{\underset{|}{C}}\right)_2\cdot \xrightarrow[\text{etc.}]{>C=C<} B{+}\left(\overset{|}{\underset{|}{C}}{-}\overset{|}{\underset{|}{C}}\right)_n\cdot}$$

I III

Step 4:

$$\mathrm{B{+}\left(\overset{|}{\underset{|}{C}}{-}\overset{|}{\underset{|}{C}}\right)_n\cdot + AB \;\longrightarrow\; B{+}\left(\overset{|}{\underset{|}{C}}{-}\overset{|}{\underset{|}{C}}\right)_n{-}A + B\cdot}$$

III IV

Radicals may be generated in any of the usual ways; the radical B· then adds to a molecule of olefin in Step 1. If the species AB is a very good transfer agent, the intermediate radical I will undergo Step 2 faster than it will add to another olefin molecule, and an excellent yield of the one-to-one product II will be produced. (Note that Steps 1 and 2 make up a chain process.) On the other hand, if AB is a poor transfer agent, and if the olefin is susceptible to radical polymerization, then Step 3 will occur faster than Step 2, and the eventual product will be IV. The sequence of Steps 1, 3, and 4 is also a chain process. It is important to recognize the consequences of the competition of AB and olefin for the monomeric radical I. If Step 2 occurs faster than Step 3, the chief product is II; if Step 3 is faster, the eventual product is the telomer IV. Clearly, the formation of the one-to-one product II will be favored by high concentrations of very reactive transfer agents and the use of olefins that are not particularly prone to polymerize. On the other hand, telomer formation will be favored by high concentrations of olefin, low concentrations of AB, and the use of polymerizable olefins and inactive transfer agents. The extreme case of a very polymerizable olefin and an inactive transfer agent may be represented by the following equations:

Step 1: $$\mathrm{B\cdot + M \xrightarrow{k_a} B{-}M\cdot}$$

Step 3: $$\mathrm{B{-}M_n\cdot + M \xrightarrow{k_p} B{-}M_{n+1}^{\bullet}}$$

Step 4: $$\mathrm{B{-}M_n\cdot + AB \xrightarrow{k_{tr}} B{-}M_n{-}A + B\cdot}$$

where M is a molecule of the olefin, B—M_n· is an abbreviation for the radical III, and B—M_n—A is an abbreviation for the telomer IV. In this case, the rate constant for Step 3 is k_p, the propagation rate constant for the polymerization of the monomer. The transfer constant C for the transfer agent AB is defined as

$$C = k_{tr}/k_p$$

If C is about 0.1 or smaller, and if AB is not present in large excess, then polymerization occurs. The value of n in A—M_n—B, called the degree of polymerization, may be 10^2 or larger; in these cases, one molecule of AB is incorporated into each large polymeric molecule. An example of this process is the polymerization of styrene in carbon tetrachloride as solvent. The transfer constant for carbon tetrachloride with styrene is 0.01, and the polymerization of styrene diluted with an equivalent number of moles of carbon tetrachloride produces a telomer with an average degree of polymerization of 70:

$$\phi CH{=}CH_2 \xrightarrow[\text{benzoyl peroxide}]{CCl_4} CCl_3{-}(CH_2{-}\underset{\phi}{\underset{|}{C}}H)_{70}{-}Cl$$

If higher ratios of styrene to carbon tetrachloride are used, polymers are produced with an average degree of polymerization approaching 10,000.

One further feature of these additions is worth pointing out. Step 1 is usually reversible, and if it is reversed faster than Step 2 or Step 3 can occur, then no addition product will be formed. This rapid, reversible addition of B· radicals, however, may isomerize *cis* olefins to *trans*. The addition of B,

$$B\cdot + \begin{matrix} R & & R \\ & C{=}C & \\ H & & H \end{matrix} \longrightarrow B{-}\underset{H}{\underset{|}{\overset{R}{\overset{|}{C}}}}{-}\dot{C}\begin{matrix} R \\ H \end{matrix}$$

produces an intermediate radical which rapidly undergoes rotation about its carbon-carbon single bond:

$$B{-}\underset{H}{\underset{|}{\overset{R}{\overset{|}{C}}}}{-}\dot{C}\begin{matrix} R \\ H \end{matrix} \rightleftharpoons B{-}\underset{H}{\underset{|}{\overset{R}{\overset{|}{C}}}}{-}\dot{C}\begin{matrix} H \\ R \end{matrix}$$

Both conformations of the radical then eliminate B, one producing a *cis* and one a *trans* olefin:

$$\mathrm{B{-}\overset{R}{\underset{H}{C}}{-}\dot{C}(R)(H)} \longrightarrow \mathrm{(R)(H)C{=}C(R)(H)} + \mathrm{B\cdot}$$

cis

$$\mathrm{B{-}\overset{R}{\underset{H}{C}}{-}\dot{C}(H)(R)} \longrightarrow \mathrm{(R)(H)C{=}C(H)(R)} + \mathrm{B\cdot}$$

trans

8.2 ADDITION OF THE HYDROGEN HALIDES AND THE HALOGENS

Hydrogen bromide is an extremely reactive hydrogen donor that adds to olefins to give excellent yields of the one-to-one adduct. This addition reaction has historical interest, since it is one of the first reactions which was shown to occur by either an ionic or a radical mechanism. In the dark, and in the absence of all radical-producing materials, hydrogen bromide slowly adds to allyl bromide by an ionic mechanism and forms the expected Markovnikov product, the 1,2-dibromide. In the presence of air, light, or any peroxidic materials, a much faster radical addition occurs, and the 1,3-dibromide is produced:

$$HBr + CH_2{=}CH{-}CH_2Br \xrightarrow[\text{darkness}]{\text{slower ionic addition,}} CH_3{-}\underset{Br}{\underset{|}{CH}}{-}CH_2Br \quad \text{ionic product}$$

$$HBr + CH_2{=}CH{-}CH_2Br \xrightarrow[\text{light, air, or peroxides}]{\text{faster radical addition,}} \underset{Br}{\underset{|}{CH_2}}{-}CH_2{-}CH_2Br \quad \text{radical product}$$

The stabilities of both radicals and carbonium ions increase in the order primary $<$ secondary $<$ tertiary. In an ionic addition of HBr, the proton adds first and forms the more stable secondary carbonium ion:

$$RCH{=}CH_2 + H^+ \longrightarrow R\overset{+}{C}H{-}CH_3 \xrightarrow{Br^-} R{-}\underset{Br}{\underset{|}{CH}}{-}CH_3$$

In the radical mechanism, a bromine atom adds first and forms the more stable secondary radical:

$$RCH{=}CH_2 + Br\cdot \longrightarrow R\dot{C}H{-}CH_2Br \xrightarrow{HBr} R{-}CH_2{-}CH_2Br + Br\cdot$$

The stereochemistry of the radical addition of hydrogen bromide has been investigated and a preference for *trans* addition is usually found. For example, deuterium bromide adds to the two isomeric 2-butenes at $-60°$ to $-78°C$ with complete stereospecificity; *cis*-2-butene gives *threo*-3-deutero-2-butane and the *trans* olefin gives the *erythro* product:

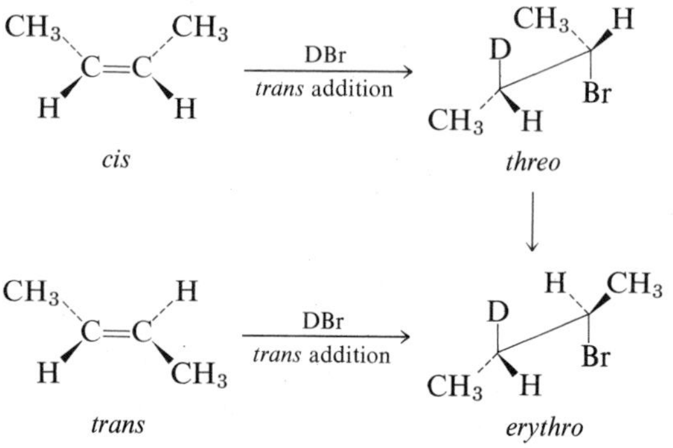

DBr
trans addition

cis *threo*

DBr
trans addition

trans *erythro*

In the 2-bromo-2-butene system, the addition of hydrogen bromide is stereospecific only at $-80°C$ in the presence of a large excess of hydrogen bromide: At higher temperatures and at lower ratios of hydrogen bromide to olefin, the stereochemical preference for *trans* addition decreases, until at 25°C the same mixture of products is obtained from either olefin. This suggests that the mechanism involves two different conformations of the intermediate radical which, if the concentration of hydrogen bromide is sufficiently low, equilibrate by rotation about the carbon-carbon bond *before* transfer occurs.

At lower temperatures and high HBr *concentrations:*

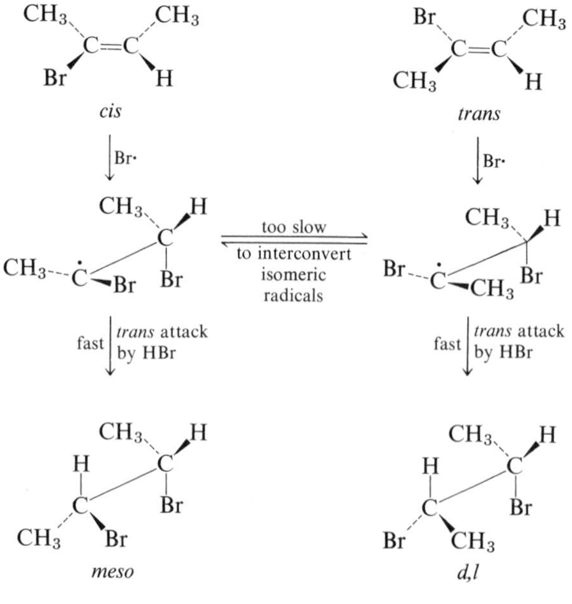

cis *trans*

Br·

too slow
to interconvert
isomeric
radicals

fast *trans* attack by HBr

meso *d,l*

At higher temperatures and low HBr *concentrations:*

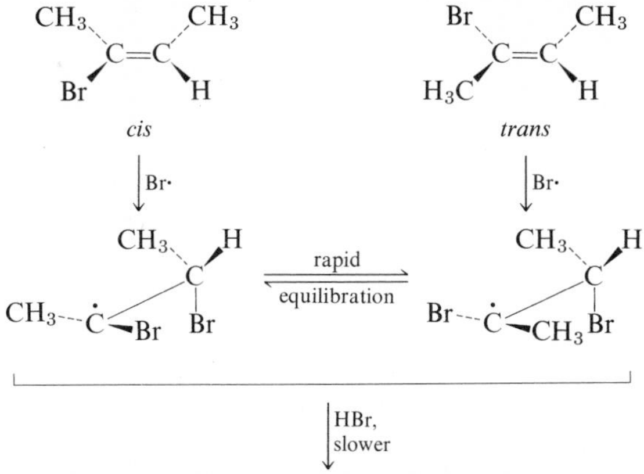

CH3 CH3 / C=C / Br H — *cis* —Br·→ radical ⇌ (rapid equilibration) radical ←Br·— *trans* — Br CH3 / C=C / H3C H

HBr, slower ↓

Same mixture of *meso* and *d,l* from either isomer.

Notice that *trans* addition is explained by assuming that the intermediate radicals are attacked by HBr from the side opposite to the α-bromine substituent.

Stereospecific *trans* addition can also be explained by assuming that bromine atoms add to an olefin via a *bridged* structure:

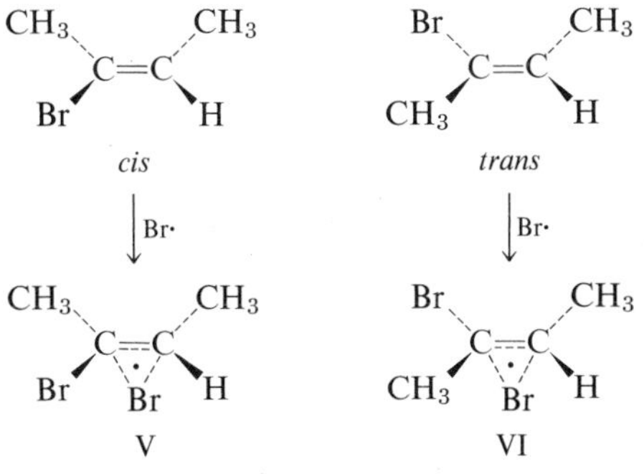

cis —Br·→ V   *trans* —Br·→ VI

If it is postulated that these bridged radicals can only be attacked by the transfer agent *trans* to the bromine bridge, then stereospecific *trans* addition results. For example, radical V from the *cis* olefin would give *meso* product:

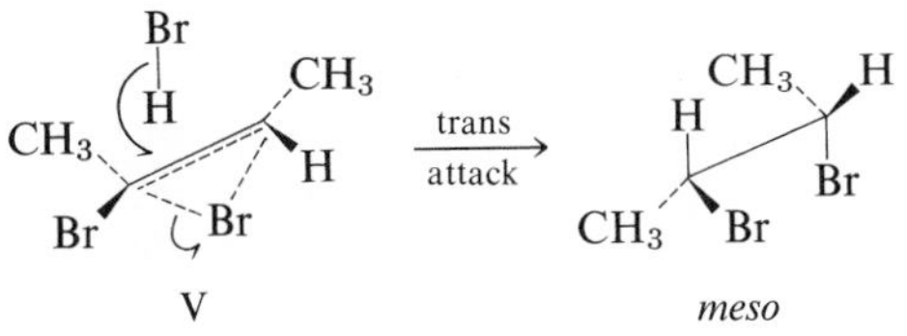

V —trans attack→ *meso*

At higher temperatures and lower hydrogen bromide concentrations, the two bridged radicals V and VI could be postulated to interconvert by a mechanism which involves open chain radicals.

Here, as in the system discussed in Sec. 2.2, p. 16, equilibration of isomeric radicals occurs under some circumstances, and open-chain radicals are necessary intermediates under these conditions. Stereoselectivity occurs under other circumstances, but bridged radicals are not specifically required even there, and they have not generally been postulated. They do, however, provide an appealingly simple explanation for attack by HBr from the side away from the original bromine atom (the *trans* direction). Furthermore, as pointed out in Sec. 2.2, there is more concrete evidence for bridged radicals in some other systems. At present, one can either postulate that *trans* addition occurs in certain open-chain radicals for reasons particular for them, or that even a small preponderence of *trans* addition is evidence for bridged radicals being intermediates under those conditions. Both views have their adherents, and this is an area of intense current research.

Steric factors can lead to a predominance of *cis* addition of hydrogen bromide to olefins. Addition to the bicyclic olefin below occurs primarily from the less hindered *exo* side:

Br·
exo attack

HBr
exo transfer

HBr
endo transfer

VII
trans

exo-cis

The main product is the *trans* dibromide VII, indicating that both the initial attack by bromine atoms and the hydrogen transfer by HBr occurred preferentially from the *exo* side.

As we have seen, radical addition of hydrogen bromide to most olefins occurs very rapidly. In contrast, radical addition of hydrogen chloride can be achieved only under special circumstances, and hydrogen iodide does not add to olefins in radical processes. Table 8-1 gives the energetics for

Table 8-1

ENERGETICS OF THE ADDITION OF THE HYDROGEN HALIDES TO ETHYLENE

$$X\cdot + CH_2{=}CH_2 \longrightarrow X{-}CH_2{-}CH_2\cdot \qquad \text{(Step 1)}\dagger$$

$$X{-}CH_2{-}CH_2\cdot + HX \longrightarrow X{-}CH_2{-}CH_3 + X\cdot \qquad \text{(Step 2)}$$

HX	ΔH (kcal/mole)	
	Step 1 (addition)	Step 2 (transfer)
HBr	−5	−11
HCl	−26	5
HI	7	−27

† See reactions on p. 71.

the addition of these three hydrogen halides to ethylene. Only in the case of hydrogen bromide are both steps exothermic. Although hydrogen iodide donates a hydrogen atom to a radical in a very exothermic step, the iodine atom is stable and does not add to olefins with release of energy. Therefore, for hydrogen iodide, Step 1 (refer to p. 71) is a bottleneck and does not occur rapidly. In the case of hydrogen chloride, the situation is reversed: the chlorine atom is very reactive and adds to olefins in a very exothermic reaction, but hydrogen chloride does not transfer a hydrogen in an exothermic step and Step 2 is the bottleneck. Thus, only hydrogen bromide is predicted to add to olefins in reactions with long chain lengths.

Radical additions of hydrogen chloride can be forced to occur under special circumstances. However, the reversibility of the reactions can lead to radical rearrangements, and radical addition of hydrogen chloride can actually produce Markovnikov products. For example, the radical addition of hydrogen chloride to propene can be envisioned to involve the following steps:

$$C{=}C{-}C \xrightarrow{Cl\cdot} \underset{\underset{\textstyle Cl}{|}}{C}{-}\dot{C}{-}C \rightleftarrows \dot{C}{-}\underset{\underset{\textstyle Cl}{|}}{C}{-}C$$

VIII   IX

VIII $\xrightarrow{\text{slow, HCl}}$ $\underset{\underset{\textstyle Cl}{|}}{CH_2}{-}CH_2{-}CH_3$ IX $\xrightarrow{\text{fast, HCl}}$ $CH_3{-}\underset{\underset{\textstyle Cl}{|}}{CH}{-}CH_3$

As the scheme above shows, although the equilibrium between VIII and IX favors VIII, transfer to the less hindered radical IX is faster than transfer to VIII, and secondary chloride is formed. Evidence for the isomerization of VIII to IX is provided by the fact that propyl chloride is converted to isopropyl chloride on irradiation with gamma rays in the presence of hydrogen chloride.

This 1,2-migration of a halogen atom is known to occur in the bromo analogue of VIII also. However, in the presence of hydrogen bromide, the transfer reaction is so fast that the first-formed radical is trapped and little or no rearrangement occurs. Therefore, hydrogen bromide adds to propene under radical conditions to give only the non-Markovnikov product:

$$\mathrm{C{=}C{-}C} \xrightarrow{\mathrm{Br}\cdot} \underset{\mathrm{Br}}{\mathrm{C}}{-}\dot{\mathrm{C}}{-}\mathrm{C} \underset{\text{to compete}}{\overset{\text{too slow}}{\not\longrightarrow}} \dot{\mathrm{C}}{-}\underset{\mathrm{Br}}{\mathrm{C}}{-}\mathrm{C}$$

$$\downarrow \text{HBr, very fast}$$

$$\underset{\mathrm{Br}}{\mathrm{CH_2}}{-}\mathrm{CH_2}{-}\mathrm{CH_3}$$

only product

The addition of the halogens to olefins can now be summarized briefly. Table 8-2 gives the energetics for the two reactions involved in the chain. Both chlorine and bromine would be predicted to add to olefins in reactions with long chain lengths, and this is found. Iodine adds only in special situations, and prefers to react with alkyl halides at the halogen atom:

$$\mathrm{I}\cdot + \mathrm{RI} \longrightarrow \mathrm{I_2} + \mathrm{R}\cdot$$

8.3 ADDITION OF THE HALOMETHANES

Table 8-3 gives data on the addition of halomethanes to olefins. The halomethanes decrease in activity as transfer agents in the order $CBr_4 > CBrCl_3 > CCl_4 > CHCl_3$. Thus, for 1-octene the yield of the one-to-one adduct decreases in this order (see Table 8-3). Styrene is much more subject to polymerization than is 1-octene, and it gives small amounts

Table 8-2

ENERGETICS OF THE ADDITION OF THE HALOGENS TO ETHYLENE

$$\mathrm{X}\cdot + \mathrm{CH_2{=}CH_2} \longrightarrow \mathrm{X{-}CH_2{-}CH_2}\cdot \qquad \text{(Step 1)}\dagger$$

$$\mathrm{X{-}CH_2{-}CH_2}\cdot + \mathrm{X_2} \longrightarrow \mathrm{X{-}CH_2{-}CH_2{-}X} + \mathrm{X}\cdot \qquad \text{(Step 2)}$$

X_2	ΔH (kcal/mole) Step 1 (addition)	Step 2 (transfer)
Br_2	−5	−17
Cl_2	−26	−19
I_2	7	−13

† See reactions on p. 71.

Table 8-3

ADDITIONS OF HALOMETHANES TO 1-OCTENE AND TO STYRENE

Halomethane	Initiator†	Product	% Yield
		Additions to 1-octene	
CBr_4	L,A	$Br_3C{-}CH_2{-}CHBr{-}C_6H_{13}$	96
$CBrCl_3$	L,A	$Cl_3C{-}CH_2{-}CHBr{-}C_6H_{13}$	88
CCl_4	A	$Cl_3C{-}CH_2{-}CHCl{-}C_6H_{13}$	85
$CHCl_3$	B	$Cl_3C{-}CH_2{-}CH_2{-}C_6H_{13}$	22
		Additions to styrene	
CBr_4	L	$Br_3C{-}CH_2{-}CHBr{-}\phi$	96
$CBrCl_3$	A	$Cl_3C{-}CH_2{-}CHBr{-}\phi$	78
		Telomer	10
CCl_4	A	Telomer	90

† L = light, A = acetyl peroxide, B = benzoyl peroxide; L,A indicates that either light or peroxide will initiate the addition.

of telomer even with a transfer agent as reactive as $CBrCl_3$. The styrene and CCl_4 mixture gives only telomer. In this case the intermediate radical adds to another styrene in preference to abstracting chlorine from carbon tetrachloride:

$$Cl_3C{-}CH_2{-}\dot{C}H\phi \xrightarrow[\text{fast}]{\phi CH=CH_2} Cl_3C{-}CH_2{-}CH\phi{-}CH_2{-}\dot{C}H\phi \longrightarrow \text{further additions lead to telomer}$$

$$Cl_3C{-}CH_2{-}\dot{C}H\phi \xrightarrow[\text{slower}]{CCl_4} Cl_3C{-}CH_2{-}CHCl\phi + \cdot CCl_3$$

8.4 ADDITION OF THIOLS AND HYDROGEN SULFIDE

Thiols and hydrogen sulfide can add to olefins either by an ionic mechanism or a radical mechanism, Markovnikov adducts being produced in one case and non-Markovnikov in the other. The ability to obtain either product gives these reactions the same synthetic utility that the hydrogen bromide additions have.

Hydrogen sulfide normally adds via an ionic mechanism; however, intense light sources such as mercury arcs or radical initiators induce the radical addition. With thiols, the radical path is the usual one, and purified materials and complete absence of light and oxygen are necessary to achieve the ionic addition. Elemental sulfur is an excellent radical scavenger, and in its presence thiols or hydrogen sulfide add to olefins by an ionic mechanism to give Markovnikov products:

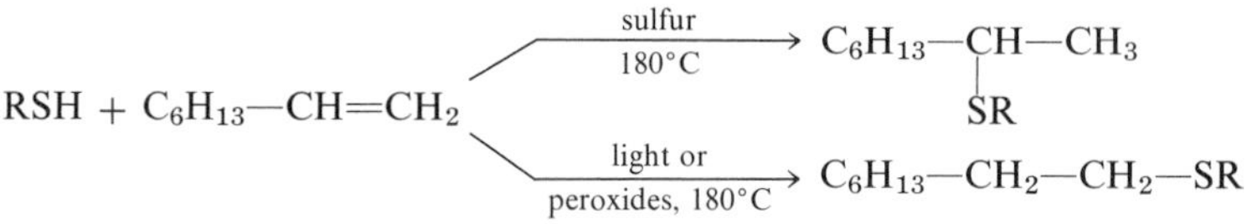
sulfur
180°C
C6H13—CH—CH3
SR
RSH + C6H13—CH=CH2
light or
peroxides, 180°C
C6H13—CH2—CH2—SR

Investigations of the stereochemistry of the addition of hydrogen sulfide to olefins have shown that stereoselective products can be obtained if high concentrations of hydrogen sulfide are present, but that stereoselectivity decreases if smaller amounts of the transfer agent are used. In the presence of high concentrations of hydrogen sulfide, the transfer rate is fast; low concentrations allow time for the two intermediate radicals to interconvert. For example, in 1-chlorocyclohexene, more *cis* product is obtained when higher concentrations of hydrogen sulfide are used (note that *cis* product results from a stereospecific *trans* addition process):

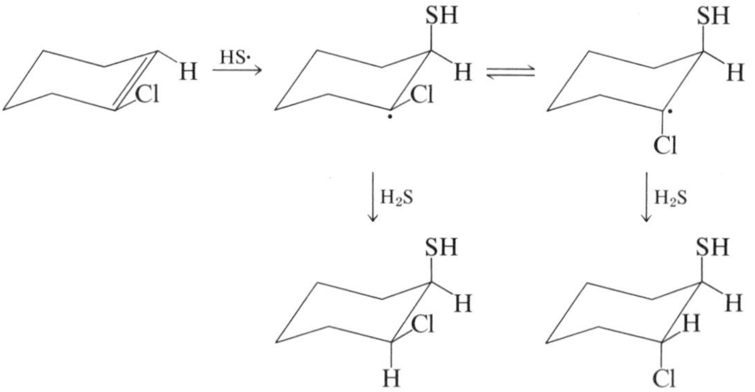
HS·
H
Cl
SH
H2S

cis *trans*

High concentrations of hydrogen sulfide trap the first radical before it inverts.

PROBLEMS

1. Explain why hydrogen bromide adds to olefins by radical mechanism much more easily than does either hydrogen chloride or hydrogen iodide.

2. Give a mechanism that explains why excess hydrogen bromide adds to the two isomeric 2-bromo-2-butenes to produce a stereospecific product at $-80°C$, whereas with lower HBr concentrations either isomer leads to the same mixture of products.

3. Why does carbon tetrachloride add to 1-octene to produce a good yield of the one-to-one product, whereas only telomer is produced with styrene? Why does CBr_4 add to both styrene and 1-octene to produce the one-to-one product? Your answer should include the competitive equations involved and a discussion of relative rates.

4. The thiyl radical from dodecanethiol, $C_{12}H_{25}S\cdot$, adds to the three olefins below with the relative rate constants shown:

Olefin	Relative rate of addition of thiyl radical
$\phi CH{=}CH_2$	17
$C_6H_{13}{-}CH{=}CH_2$	1.0
$CH_2Cl{-}CH{=}CH_2$	0.7

Rationalize this pattern of relative rates. (Hint: consider the stability and possible polar resonance structures of the transition states.)

5. When hydrogen sulfide is present in high concentrations, it adds to 1-chlorocyclohexene to give the *cis* adduct. Rationalize this result assuming that H_2S adds *via* a bridged radical intermediate. How do you then explain the lack of stereospecificity when lower H_2S concentrations are used?

9
Radical Polymerizations

The progress made in polymer chemistry since the 1930's is one of the most significant accomplishments of chemical research in recent years. A glance around an average room reveals man-made fabrics, structural materials, table tops, dishes, and many other items which only a few years ago would have been produced from wood, metal, or other natural products.

Synthetic polymers can be made by either ionic or by radical processes. Some of the commerical plastics are produced by both processes, but most utilize one or the other. The subject of ionic polymerization is beyond the bounds of this text†, and a detailed discussion of radical polymerization is more suited to an advanced textbook. However, certain types of information about free radicals can best be obtained by studies of polymeric radicals, and it is important that these be discussed here. First, however, it will be interesting to examine the range of useful plastics that can be produced by radical polymerization processes.

9.1 EXAMPLES OF USEFUL POLYMERS

Polymerization reactions are divided into two types. Most free radical polymerizations are *addition polymerizations,* in which the repeating unit in the chain, the "mer," is identical with the monomer. The simplest example is polyethylene‡:

$$nCH_2{=}CH_2 \longrightarrow \left(CH_2{-}CH_2 \right)_n$$

Some ionic polymers are formed by addition polymerizations, but most are formed in *condensation polymerizations.* In this type of reaction, a small molecule is split from the reacting monomers. An example is the formation

† Polymers are discussed in the volume in this series by J. Stille, *Industrial Organic Chemistry* (in preparation).

‡ Notice that the nature of the end of the polymeric chain is not specified. Polymer molecules have very high molecular weights and, consequently, a very small number of end groups per mole of polymer molecules. Usually, the experimental determination of the nature of these end groups is very difficult, but their nature can be inferred from the mechanism by which the polymer molecules are formed. We will consider these mechanisms later in this chapter.

of nylon from adipic acid and hexamethylenediamine, where water is eliminated:

$$n\mathrm{CO_2H{-}(CH_2)_4{-}CO_2H} + n\mathrm{NH_2{-}(CH_2)_6{-}NH_2} \longrightarrow \left(\overset{\displaystyle \mathrm{O}}{\overset{\|}{\mathrm{C}}}\mathrm{{-}(CH_2)_4{-}}\overset{\displaystyle \mathrm{O}}{\overset{\|}{\mathrm{C}}}\mathrm{{-}}\overset{\displaystyle \mathrm{H}}{\overset{|}{\mathrm{N}}}\mathrm{{-}(CH_2)_6{-}}\overset{\displaystyle \mathrm{H}}{\overset{|}{\mathrm{N}}}\right)_n + 2n\mathrm{H_2O}$$

In this text we shall restrict our discussion to addition polymerization by radical mechanisms.

The simplest and one of the most useful polymers is polyethylene. Two processes are used for producing this polymer. The older radical process gives material, called "high pressure" polyethylene, that melts at about 110°C; the newer ionic process gives material, called either "low pressure" or "high density" polyethylene, that has a melting point of about 130°C. Despite the somewhat broader utility of the higher melting, stiffer material produced by the ionic process, the radical process is still used because it produces a more transparent product which is superior in certain applications. In the radical process, ethylene at about 1000 atm is heated to 200°C in the presence of a small, controlled amount of air or peroxide, and polymer is removed continuously. The air or peroxide reacts with ethylene to produce radicals (Reaction (9-1)). These primary radicals then add to the monomer to initiate the polymerization (Reaction (9-2)). The resulting radical, which contains one monomer unit, adds another to produce a dimer, which reacts to form a trimer, etc.:

$$\mathrm{CH_2{=}CH_2} \xrightarrow[\text{peroxide}]{\text{air or}} \text{radicals } (\mathrm{R}\cdot) \tag{9-1}$$

$$\mathrm{R}\cdot + \mathrm{CH_2{=}CH_2} \longrightarrow \mathrm{R{-}CH_2{-}\dot{C}H_2} \tag{9-2}$$

$$\mathrm{R{-}(CH_2{-}CH_2)_n}\cdot + \mathrm{CH_2{=}CH_2} \longrightarrow \mathrm{R{-}(CH_2{-}CH_2)_n{-}CH_2{-}\dot{C}H_2} \tag{9-3}$$

$$2\sim\mathrm{CH_2{-}CH_2}\cdot \xrightarrow{\text{combination}} \sim\mathrm{CH_2{-}CH_2{-}CH_2{-}CH_2}\sim \tag{9-4}$$

$$2\sim\mathrm{CH_2{-}CH_2}\cdot \xrightarrow[\text{tionation}]{\text{dispropor-}} \sim\mathrm{CH{=}CH_2} + \sim\mathrm{CH_2{-}CH_3} \tag{9-5}$$

Finally, growth is stopped when two chains interact either by combination (9-4) or by disproportionation (9-5). (The wavy line indicates the polymer chain.) Polyethylene has been produced commercially in the United States since 1943. Today it is used in sheeting, films, flexible bottles, trays, as a coating and insulation for electrical wires, and in many other applications.

Notice that the essential features of this polymerization are the formation of a reactive end by an initiation process, the growth of this end in reactions of low activation energy, and then termination and formation of the polymer:

Initiation:	initiator $\longrightarrow$ M·
Propagation:	M· + M $\longrightarrow$ M_2· $\xrightarrow{\text{etc.}}$ M_n·
Termination:	$2M_n$· $\longrightarrow$ polymer

where M is a molecule of olefin (monomer) and M_n· is a radical containing *n* olefin units. This formation and growth of a reactive end is the key feature of radical addition polymerization. The growth reactions are extremely fast: several thousand monomer units are added in just a few seconds, and then termination occurs. Polymers formed in radical processes usually have 10^2 to 10^5 repeat units per molecule and molecular weights of 10^4 to 10^7.

Substitution of different groups for one or more of the hydrogens in ethylene produces monomers that lead to other useful polymers. The substitution of four fluorines produces tetrafluoroethene, which forms a polymer called Teflon:

$$n\mathrm{CF_2{=}CF_2} \xrightarrow[\text{polymerization}]{\text{radical}} \mathrm{-\!\!(CF_2{-}CF_2)\!\!-_{\it n}}$$

Teflon is produced by a radical process not unlike that used for polyethylene itself. Teflon's low coefficient-of-friction and high thermal stability make it useful in applications such as greaseless bearings, liners for skillets, containers for very reactive chemicals, and the coating for the undersides of skis.

Trifluorochloroethene polymerizes to give materials similar to, but more rigid than, Teflon. These materials are called Kel-F or Fluorothene:

$$n\mathrm{CF_2{=}CFCl} \xrightarrow[\text{polymerization}]{\text{radical}} \mathrm{-\!\!(CF_2{-}CFCl)\!\!-_{\it n}}$$

Vinyl chloride, $CH_2{=}CHCl$, is one of the most useful monomers. Polyvinyl chloride is sold under names such as Exon, Geon, Koroseal, and Tygon, and is usually the plastic referred to when "vinyl plastics" are sold. Vinyl chloride is readily polymerized by peroxide or azo compounds at 50 to 80°C. The polymer is insoluble in the monomer, and precipitates as formed:

$$n\mathrm{CH_2{=}CHCl} \longrightarrow \left(\mathrm{CH_2{-}\underset{}{\overset{\displaystyle Cl}{\overset{|}{C}}}H}\right)_n$$

Polyvinyl chloride is a brittle, hard material that is insoluble and fairly rigid. It is used for pipes, rods, and in sheeting. The plastic also has the useful property of being easily "plasticized"; that is, when organic materials such as esters are mixed with it, the hard plastic is converted to a flexible, transparent, rubbery material. This plasticized "vinyl" is used for shower curtains, garden hose, power cable insulation, food coverings, toys, Leatherette and laboratory tubing.

Vinylidene chloride, $CH_2{=}CCl_2$, can be polymerized in much the same way. This polymer is chiefly used in polymer mixtures. These polymer mixtures, or copolymers, frequently have physical properties that are better than either of the pure polymers. The vinylidene chloride-vinyl chloride copolymer is marketed under the name Saran.

Methyl methacrylate can be polymerized by radical initiators to produce a polymer of great clarity that is sold under the names Lucite, Plexiglas, and Perspex:

$$n\,\underset{\displaystyle CH_3}{\overset{\displaystyle CO_2CH_3}{\overset{|}{\underset{|}{C}}}}{=}CH_2 \longrightarrow \left(\underset{\displaystyle CH_3}{\overset{\displaystyle CO_2CH_3}{\overset{|}{\underset{|}{C}}}}-CH_2\right)_n$$

Poly(methyl methacrylate) is used for contact lenses, plastic window domes, automobile taillight lenses, and other products in which transparency and clarity are desired.

Acrylonitrile is polymerized by radical initiators in an aqueous emulsion system:

$$n\,\overset{\displaystyle C{\equiv}N}{\overset{|}{C}H}{=}CH_2 \longrightarrow \left(\overset{\displaystyle C{\equiv}N}{\overset{|}{C}H}-CH_2\right)_n$$

The polyacrylonitrile which was introduced in 1948 under the name Orlon was the first usable fiber made by an addition polymerization. Dynel, a more recent fiber, is a copolymer of about 60% vinyl chloride and 40% acrylonitrile.

Styrene can be polymerized by radical sources to give the clear, somewhat brittle polystyrene:

$$n\phi CH{=}CH_2 \longrightarrow \left(\overset{\displaystyle \phi}{\overset{|}{C}H}-CH_2\right)_n$$

It is sold under the names of Lustrex and Styron, and can be molded into sheets and fibers (Polyflex, Styroflex). If the polymer is melted, and if air is then blown through it while it cools, a solid foam is produced which has varying densities according to the preparation procedure. Polystyrene itself is rather brittle, but its butadiene copolymers are more flexible. The copolymer that contains 75% butadiene is the main synthetic rubber used in tires; it is produced by radical emulsion polymerization. Copolymers containing less butadiene are more rigid but less brittle than are polymers of pure styrene. Copolymers that are about 80% styrene are used for shoe heels, flooring, golf ball covers, football helmets, bowling balls, and luggage. Copolymers of about 73% styrene and 27% acrylonitrile are used for plastic dishes.

9.2 KINETICS OF POLYMERIZATIONS

The mechanism for polymerization of a monomer can be summarized by the equations below:

Initiation:

$$\text{radical source} \longrightarrow \text{R}\cdot \tag{9-6}$$

$$\text{R}\cdot + \text{M} \xrightarrow{k_i} \text{M}\cdot \tag{9-7}$$

Propagation:

$$\text{M}\cdot + \text{M} \xrightarrow{k_p} \text{M}_2\cdot \tag{9-8}$$

or, in general,

$$\text{M}_n\cdot + \text{M} \xrightarrow{k_p} \text{M}_{n+1}\cdot \tag{9-9}$$

Termination:

by combination

$$\text{M}_n\cdot + \text{M}_m\cdot \xrightarrow{k_t} \text{M}_n\text{—M}_m \tag{9-10}$$

by disproportionation

$$\text{M}_n\cdot + \text{M}_m\cdot \xrightarrow{k_t} \text{M}_n + \text{M}_m\text{—H} \tag{9-11}$$

where R· is a low molecular weight radical, $M_n\cdot$ and $M_m\cdot$ are polymeric radicals containing n or m units of the monomer, and M_n is an olefin. Notice the assumption that the reactivity of a radical is independent of the number of monomer units in its chain. Thus, for example, the rate constants of the two propagation steps shown below are assumed to be equal:

$$\text{M}\cdot + \text{M} \longrightarrow \text{M—M}\cdot$$

$$\text{M}_{50}\cdot + \text{M} \longrightarrow \text{M}_{51}\cdot$$

Obviously this is a simplification, but it leads to a number of useful kinetic equations. Since all radicals are equivalent, they can be abbreviated M· and the subscript omitted. Kinetic equations for free radical systems can be simplified further through use of the *steady-state approximation.* Since most radicals are highly reactive species, their concentrations will be very small, and consequently the rate of change in their concentrations also will be small. In the steady-state approximation, the rate of change in the concentration of a reactive species is set equal to zero; in other words, its rate of formation is set equal to its rate of destruction. At the steady-state in the concentration of M· radicals, their rate of formation equals the rate at which termination reactions occur. Let us call R_i the rate of formation of M·, and call the total rate of destruction of M· (the sum of Reactions (9-10) and (9-11)) $2k_t(\mathrm{M}\cdot)^2$. (The 2 accounts for the fact that each termination reaction destroys 2M· radicals.) Then at the steady state,

$$R_i = 2k_t(\mathrm{M}\cdot)^2$$

or

$$(\mathrm{M}\cdot) = \frac{R_i^{1/2}}{(2k_t)^{1/2}} \tag{9-12}$$

The rate of formation of polymer, R_P, is equal to the rate of disappearance of monomer. Monomer is used in Reactions (9-7) and (9-9), but since the chains are very long, to an excellent approximation monomer is used only in Reaction (9-9). Therefore, the rate of formation of polymer is given by

$$R_P = k_p(\mathrm{M})(\mathrm{M}\cdot)$$

and substitution of Equation (9-12) leads to

$$R_P = k_p(\mathrm{M})\frac{R_i^{1/2}}{(2k_t)^{1/2}} \tag{9-13}$$

This equation predicts that the rate of formation of polymer is directly proportional to the concentration of monomer, and this has been verified in a number of systems. Equation (9-13) also leads to the prediction that the rate of growth of polymer is independent of the chemical nature of the initiator. This is quite reasonable: the initiator determines the rate of formation of M· radicals, but the rate of growth of polymer depends on the nature of the monomer and its concentration.

If species that undergo atom-transfer with the growing polymeric radical are present, then polymer molecule chain ends can be produced by this process as well as by the usual termination process. For example, if a solvent SH is present, the *chain transfer* step shown below can occur:

$$\mathrm{M}_n\cdot + S\mathrm{H} \longrightarrow \mathrm{M}_n\text{—H} + S\cdot$$

The new radical then reinitiates growth:

$$S\cdot + \mathrm{M} \longrightarrow S\text{—M}\cdot \tag{9-14}$$

Chain transfer lowers the average molecular weight of the polymer because it converts a growing polymeric radical to a polymer molecule. However, if the reinitiation step (9-14) occurs rapidly, the rate at which monomer is converted to polymer is not affected. The essential feature of chain transfer is that the growing polymeric radical can react either with another monomer molecule or with the transfer agent SH:

$$M_n\cdot + M \xrightarrow{k_p} M_{n+1}\cdot$$

$$M_n\cdot + SH \xrightarrow{k_{tr}} M_n\text{—}H + S\cdot$$

Thus, it is convenient to measure the effectiveness of transfer agents by their transfer constant $C = k_{tr}/k_p$ (Sec. 8.1, p. 72). Table 9-1 gives the transfer constants for a series of transfer agents in styrene and vinyl acetate polymerizations. The structures of the growing polymeric radicals in these two cases are shown below:

$$\sim CH_2\text{—}\overset{\displaystyle H}{\underset{\displaystyle \phi}{C}}\cdot \qquad\qquad \sim CH_2\text{—}\overset{\displaystyle H}{\underset{\displaystyle O\text{—}C(=O)\text{—}CH_3}{C}}\cdot$$

radical from styrene — radical from vinyl acetate

where the heavy wavy line represents the remainder of the polymeric molecule. Most of the transfer agents listed in Table 9-1 undergo transfer by hydrogen abstraction. Notice that the hydrogens are transferred in the usual order, namely primary < secondary < tertiary. Butanethiol and hydrogen sulfide are particularly effective hydrogen donors. Halogen

Table 9-1

TRANSFER CONSTANTS AT 60°C FOR REACTIONS INVOLVING THE RADICAL FROM STYRENE OR VINYL ACETATE

Transfer agent	Transfer constant	
	Styrene	Vinyl acetate
Benzene	0.6×10^{-5}	—
Toluene	1.6×10^{-5}	—
Isopropylbenzene	1.8×10^{-4}	—
Cyclohexane	0.4×10^{-5}	7.0×10^{-4}
Diphenylmethane	2.8×10^{-4}	—
Triphenylmethane	6.5×10^{-4}	—
Isopropyl alcohol	0.8×10^{-4}	—
Butyraldehyde	5.7×10^{-4}	6.5×10^{-2}
Acetone	0.5×10^{-4}	1.2×10^{-3}
Methyl disulfide	9.4×10^{-3}	—
Carbon tetrabromide	2.2	$\sim 0.4 \times 10^{2}$
Carbon tetrachloride	1.1×10^{-2}	—
Butanethiol	2.2×10^{1}	4.8×10^{1}
Hydrogen sulfide	$\sim 0.5 \times 10^{1}$	—
Styrene	0.8×10^{-4}	—
Vinyl acetate	—	2.2×10^{-4}

atoms are abstracted from carbon tetrabromide and carbon tetrachloride. Note that the polymeric radical even abstracts hydrogen atoms from its own monomer, although neither styrene nor vinyl acetate is particularly effective as a transfer agent. Methyl disulfide is a fairly good transfer agent; in this case much of the transfer occurs through a reaction on sulfur:

$$\mathrm{M}_n\cdot + \mathrm{RSSR} \longrightarrow \mathrm{M}_n\mathrm{SR} + \mathrm{RS}\cdot$$

This is one of the few transfer reactions which occurs on an atom that is not univalent.

9.3 COPOLYMERIZATION

Many useful plastics are produced by allowing two or more monomers to polymerize together. In this way, the properties of each polymer are blended, and plastics are tailored to particular applications. Copolymerization, therefore, has great commercial interest, and all the common monomers have been studied in mixtures with each other. Copolymerization is also important because it allows study of the factors that influence the relative rates of addition of radicals to olefins. In a copolymerization, two different olefins compete for the growing polymeric radicals. Although the system is complicated by the fact that two different radicals are present, a rather simple analysis allows relative reactivities to be obtained. The reactions which occur when two monomers copolymerize are summarized below:

	Rate
$\mathrm{M_1\cdot + M_1 \longrightarrow M_1\cdot}$	$k_{11}(\mathrm{M_1\cdot})(\mathrm{M_1})$
$\mathrm{M_1\cdot + M_2 \longrightarrow M_2\cdot}$	$k_{12}(\mathrm{M_1\cdot})(\mathrm{M_2})$
$\mathrm{M_2\cdot + M_1 \longrightarrow M_1\cdot}$	$k_{21}(\mathrm{M_2\cdot})(\mathrm{M_1})$
$\mathrm{M_2\cdot + M_2 \longrightarrow M_2\cdot}$	$k_{22}(\mathrm{M_2\cdot})(\mathrm{M_2})$

where $\mathrm{M_1}$ is the first monomer, $\mathrm{M_2}$ is the second, and $\mathrm{M_1\cdot}$ and $\mathrm{M_2\cdot}$ are the polymeric radicals that have monomer 1 or monomer 2 on the end of the chain. If we assume that the reactivity of the polymeric radical depends only on the end monomer, and not on the composition of the rest of the chain, and also that a steady-state in radical concentrations exists, then the following copolymerization equation can be derived:

$$\frac{d(\mathrm{M_1})}{d(\mathrm{M_2})} = \frac{(\mathrm{M_1})}{(\mathrm{M_2})}\left[\frac{r_1(\mathrm{M_1}) + (\mathrm{M_2})}{(\mathrm{M_1}) + r_2(\mathrm{M_2})}\right]$$

where r_1 and r_2 are defined as shown below:

$$r_1 = k_{11}/k_{12}$$

$$r_2 = k_{22}/k_{21}$$

Table 9-2

COPOLYMER REACTIVITY RATIOS AT 60°C

M_1	M_2	r_1	r_2
Styrene	Methyl methacrylate	0.5	0.5
Styrene	*p*-Nitrostyrene	0.2	1.1
Styrene	*p*-Chlorostyrene	0.7	1.0
Styrene	*p*-Methoxystyrene	1.2	0.8
Styrene	Acrylonitrile	0.4	0.04
Styrene	Vinyl acetate	55	0.01
Styrene	Ethyl vinyl ether	90	~0
Styrene	Butadiene	0.78	1.4
Styrene	Vinyl chloride	17	0.02
Vinyl acetate	Vinyl chloride	0.2	1.7
Vinyl acetate	Methyl methacrylate	0.01	20

The copolymerization equation given above relates the rate of incorporation of the two monomers to their concentrations and to r_1 and r_2. The parameters r_1 and r_2 are called monomer reactivity ratios. When $r_1 > 1$, the polymeric radical ending with monomer 1 will react with its own monomer faster than with monomer 2; when $r_1 < 1$, the polymeric radical ending in monomer 1 will react faster with monomer 2. In the special case in which $r_1 = r_2 = 1$, the polymeric radical shows no preference for either monomer, regardless of which one is on the end of the chain, and the two monomers will be distributed randomly along the chain in a ratio that depends only on the ratio of monomer concentrations in the reaction mixture. If r_1 and r_2 are both very small, the polymer will have alternating units of monomer 1 and 2.

Table 9-2 gives values of some typical reactivity ratios. For example, in the styrene-methyl methacrylate system, both r_1 and r_2 equal 0.5, meaning that each polymeric radical has about twice as much tendency to react with the opposite monomer as with its own. This type of alternation effect is best explained as being due to polar influences.

PROBLEMS

1. Draw in detail the reactions that occur when *t*-butyl peroxide is used to initiate the polymerization of styrene. (The termination mechanism for styrene is known to be almost entirely combination.)

2. Describe the experimental procedure for measuring the ratio of rate constants $k_p/k_t^{1/2}$ for styrene. Why is this ratio of rate constants particularly easy to obtain? (Hint: are radical concentrations involved in your equations?) This ratio is used to measure the polymerizability of an olefin. What is the significance of a large value for this ratio?

3. Write the chemical reactions that occur when the polystyryl radical undergoes chain transfer with the following chain transfer agents: benzaldehyde, hydrogen sulfide, acetone, triphenylmethane, styrene, chloroform, methyl iodide, isopropyl alcohol, and diphenyl disulfide.

4. Given an explanation for the fact that the copolymer of styrene and methyl methacrylate consists largely of alternating units of the two monomers along the chain. (Hint: consider polar structures of the transition states involved.)

5. Note that the ratio $k_p/k_t^{1/2}$ occurs in (9-13). Why does this ratio appear rather than k_p/k_t?

6. In radical polymerizations, the propagation step, which involves the addition of a radical to an olefin, has a low activation energy and is fast, and chain lengths of several thousand units are attained in several seconds so that high polymers are produced. However, the termination reaction, which involves the coupling of two free radicals, has an even lower activation energy than the propagation step. Therefore, why don't radicals instantly couple upon formation, and thus not allow any growth at all to occur?

7. Use the copolymerization equation to prove that the composition of the copolymer approaches a one-to-one mixture of the two monomers as r_1 and r_2 both approach zero. Explain in words why this should be true.

SUGGESTED FURTHER READINGS

Ferington, T. E., "Kinetics of Polymer Formation by Free Radical Mechanisms," *J. Chem. Ed.,* **35**(1959), 174.

Mayo, F. R., "Contributions of Vinyl Polymerization to Organic Chemistry," *J. Chem. Ed.,* **36**(1959), 157.

Moore, W. J., *Physical Chemistry* (3rd ed.). Englewood Cliffs, N.J.: Prentice-Hall, Inc., 1963. See Chap. 19.

10 Aromatic Substitution

In electrophilic aromatic substitution reactions, the familiar pattern is that electron-donating groups, such as alkyl or alkoxy, are *ortho*- and *para*-directing and lead to enhanced rates of substitution, whereas electron-withdrawing groups, such as nitro, lead to *meta* substitution products and deactivation of the ring. In contrast to this, in some homolytic aromatic substitution *all* substituents lead to faster rates of reaction. The orientation rules also are different in the radical process; for example, both the methyl and the nitro group can be *para*-directing. The different products from the two mechanisms may be illustrated by the data below:

Cl—C₆H₅ $\xrightarrow[\text{HNO}_3\text{—H}_2\text{SO}_4]{\text{nitration by the } NO_2^+ \text{ ion from}}$ *o*-Cl—C₆H₄—NO₂ 31%, *m*-Cl—C₆H₄—NO₂ 0%, *p*-Cl—C₆H₄—NO₂ 69%

Cl—C₆H₅ $\xrightarrow[\text{peroxide}]{\text{phenylation by } \phi\cdot \text{ from benzoyl}}$ *o*-Cl—C₆H₄—ϕ 50%, *m*-Cl—C₆H₄—ϕ 32%, *p*-Cl—C₆H₄—ϕ 18%

The nitration of chlorobenzene by the electrophilic NO_2^+ ion gives mainly *para* products. Further, since a halogen is a slightly deactivating substituent (although *ortho-para*-directing), chlorobenzene is attacked only 0.03 times as fast as benzene itself. In the phenylation of chlorobenzene, where a neutral phenyl radical is the attacking species, the product is mainly *ortho* substituted, and chlorobenzene reacts about 1.4 times faster than benzene.

10.1 PHENYLATION

The homolytic substitution reaction that has been studied with the most thoroughness is phenylation. The phenyl radical can be generated in several ways, as is shown below:

$$\phi\text{—}\overset{\overset{\displaystyle O}{\|}}{C}\text{—O—O—}\overset{\overset{\displaystyle O}{\|}}{C}\text{—}\phi \longrightarrow 2\phi CO_2\cdot \longrightarrow 2\phi\cdot + 2CO_2 \qquad (10\text{-}1a)$$

$$\phi\text{—}\underset{}{\overset{\overset{\displaystyle N=O}{|}}{N}}\text{—CO—CH}_3 \longrightarrow \phi\cdot + N_2 + CH_3CO_2\cdot \qquad (10\text{-}1b)$$

$$\phi\text{—N=N—C}\phi_3 \longrightarrow \phi\cdot + N_2 + \phi_3C\cdot \qquad (10\text{-}1c)$$

$$\phi N_2^+Cl^- + NaOH \longrightarrow \phi\cdot + N_2 + NaCl + OH\cdot \qquad (10\text{-}1d)$$

$$\phi_3Bi \longrightarrow 3\phi\cdot + Bi \qquad (10\text{-}1e)$$

Phenyl radicals from any of these sources can phenylate aromatic compounds:

$$\text{Ar—H} \xrightarrow{\phi\cdot} \text{Ar—}\phi \qquad (10\text{-}2)$$

Reaction (10-1a) is the familiar decomposition of benzoyl peroxide; when the decomposition occurs in an aromatic solvent, nuclear substitution of the solvent occurs as shown in Reaction (10-2). The product is the result of attack on the solvent by phenyl radicals from the peroxide; very little, if any, of the other two possible products are formed. For example, if the solvent is Ar—H, the products are

$$\text{Ar—H} \xrightarrow{\phi\cdot} \underset{\text{(mainly)}}{\text{Ar—}\phi} + \underset{\text{(much less)}}{\phi\text{—}\phi + \text{Ar—Ar}}$$

In Reaction (10-1b), N-nitrosoacetanilide, prepared by nitrosation of acetanilide with nitrosyl chloride, rearranges to the diazoester:

$$\phi\text{—}\overset{\overset{\displaystyle N=O}{|}}{N}\text{—CO—CH}_3 \xrightarrow{\text{rearrangement}} \phi\text{—N=N—O—}\overset{\overset{\displaystyle O}{\|}}{C}\text{—CH}_3$$

The diazoester undergoes rapid homolysis to produce phenyl radicals:

$$\phi\text{—N=N—O—}\overset{\overset{\displaystyle O}{\|}}{C}\text{—CH}_3 \longrightarrow \phi\cdot + N_2 + CH_3\text{—}CO_2\cdot$$

In Reaction (10-1c), phenylazotriphenylmethane is the phenyl source. The stable trityl radical does not interfere in the phenylation reaction. In Reaction (10-1d), the so-called Gomberg reaction, diazonium salts, produced by the diazotization of aniline with nitrous acid, are used as a radical source. In Reaction (10-1e), triphenylbismuth is the phenyl radical source. Other organometallics can also be used.

Table 10-1 gives data for the phenylation of a number of substrates using three of these initiators as sources of phenyl radicals. Phenyl radicals from all three sources give about the same rate ratio for phenylation of toluene relative to benzene. It is generally observed that different precursors of phenyl radicals give similar, but not identical, product composi-

Table 10-1

RELATIVE RATES OF PHENYLATION OF SUBSTITUTED BENZENES

X in ϕ—X	Phenyl source		
	Benzoyl peroxide 70°C	ϕ—N(NO)—$COCH_3$ 20°C	ϕ_3Bi photolysis 80°C
NO_2	4.0	3.1	—
H	(1.0)	(1.0)	(1.0)
Cl	1.4	1.5	—
Br	1.7	1.8	—
CH_3	1.7†	1.8	1.7

† Hydrogen abstraction from the methyl group occurs to the extent of about 15%.

tions and rate ratios. Note that nitrobenzene, chlorobenzene, bromobenzene, and toluene are all phenylated faster than is benzene. The rate differences, however, are *much* smaller than would be observed in typical electrophilic ionic substitutions.

10.2 BENZOYL PEROXIDE

Benzoyl peroxide has been studied more than any other phenylating agent, and more data are available on isomer distribution, rates, and mechanisms for this initiator than for any other. Table 10-2 gives typical isomer distribution figures. Notice that *ortho* substitution is preferred for all of the substituents.

The extensive study of benzoyl peroxide has led to a good understanding of the processes in which it reacts with aromatic substances. The mechanism involves an addition by phenyl radicals to the double bonds of

Table 10-2

ISOMER DISTRIBUTION OF PRODUCTS FROM THE PHENYLATION OF ϕ—X USING BENZOYL PEROXIDE AT 80°C

X in ϕ—X	Isomer % in X—C_6H_4—ϕ		
	ortho	*meta*	*para*
NO_2	62	10	28
Cl	50	32	18
Br	49	33	18
CH_3	67	19	14

the aromatic solvent, followed by hydrogen transfer steps. This is illustrated for the phenylation of benzene below:

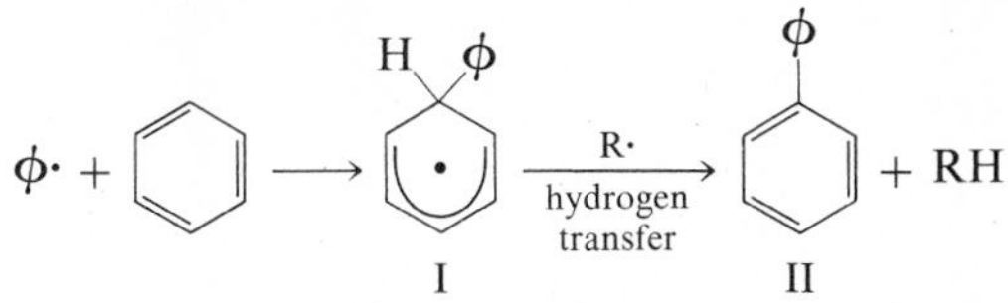

$$\phi\cdot + C_6H_6 \longrightarrow \text{I} \xrightarrow[\text{hydrogen transfer}]{R\cdot} \text{II} + RH$$

The occurrence of the intermediate radical I is indicated by the isolation of its combination and disproportionation products. For example, the decomposition of a 0.01*M* solution of benzoyl peroxide in benzene gives the products

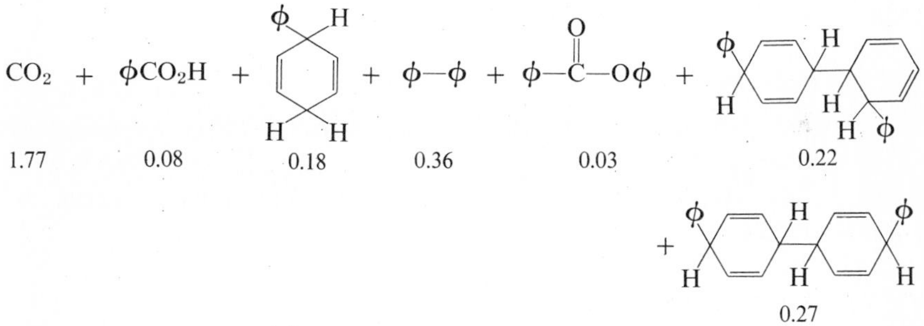

$$\underset{1.77}{CO_2} + \underset{0.08}{\phi CO_2H} + \underset{0.18}{\text{(dihydrobiphenyl)}} + \underset{0.36}{\phi\text{—}\phi} + \underset{0.03}{\phi\text{—}\overset{O}{\overset{\|}{C}}\text{—}O\phi} + \underset{0.22}{\text{(tetrahydroquaterphenyl)}} + \underset{0.27}{\text{(tetrahydroquaterphenyl)}}$$

where the numbers under the products indicate yield in moles per mole of peroxide. The cyclohexadienyl products clearly result from various reactions of the intermediate radical I. For example:

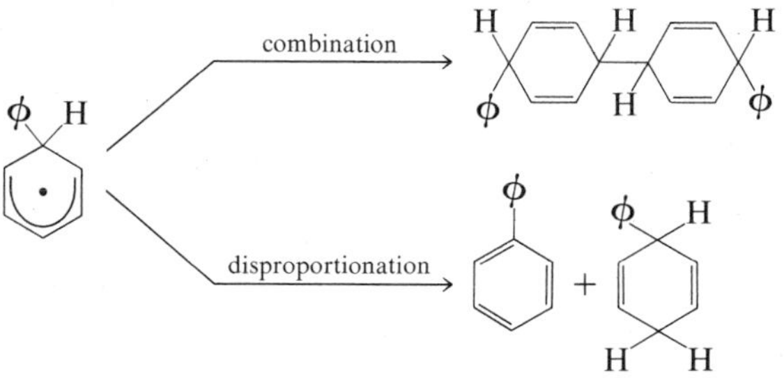

combination → (dimer); disproportionation → ϕ-benzene + dihydrobiphenyl

The mechanism for the formation of phenyl benzoate may be envisioned as occurring in one of three ways:

$$\phi\cdot + \phi CO_2\text{—}CO_2\phi \longrightarrow \phi CO_2\phi + \phi CO_2\cdot \quad \text{(10-3a)}$$

$$\phi CO_2\text{—}CO_2\phi \longrightarrow \phi CO_2\phi + CO_2 \quad \text{(10-3b)}$$

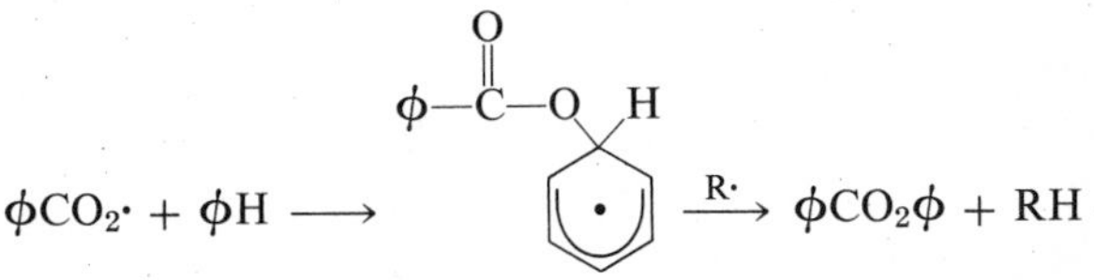

$$\phi CO_2\cdot + \phi H \longrightarrow \text{(}\phi\text{—}\overset{O}{\overset{\|}{C}}\text{—O, H cyclohexadienyl radical)} \xrightarrow{R\cdot} \phi CO_2\phi + RH \quad \text{(10-3c)}$$

Table 10-3

RELATIVE RATES FOR ARYLATION OF NITROBENZENE AND TOLUENE BY VARIOUS ARYL RADICALS AT 80°C†

Substrate	Radical: p-NO_2-phenyl	p-Cl-phenyl	phenyl	p-CH_3-phenyl
Nitrobenzene	0.9	1.5	4.0	5.1
Benzene	(1)	(1)	(1)	(1)
Toluene	2.6	1.3	1.7	1.0

† The radicals are generated from substituted benzoyl peroxides.

Reaction (10-3a) is an induced decomposition, (10-3b) is a cage decomposition, and (10-3c) is the addition reaction effected by benzoate instead of by phenyl radicals. Reaction (10-3a) undoubtedly occurs in concentrated solutions, and it is probable that ester is also formed by the cage reaction, (10-3b), under some conditions. In these 0.01*M* solutions, however, Reaction (10-3c) apparently is the main path responsible for ester formation. This follows from the fact that *p*-chlorobenzoyl peroxide gives only phenyl *p*-chlorobenzoate and no *p*-chlorophenyl *p*-chlorobenzoate:

$$\underset{\text{(Ar is }p\text{-chlorophenyl)}}{\mathrm{Ar\overset{O}{\overset{\|}{C}}{-}O{-}O{-}\overset{O}{\overset{\|}{C}}Ar}} \xrightarrow{\text{benzene}} \underset{\text{(formed)}}{\phi\mathrm{O{-}\overset{O}{\overset{\|}{C}}Ar}} + \underset{\text{(not formed)}}{\mathrm{ArO{-}\overset{O}{\overset{\|}{C}}Ar}}$$

It should be pointed out that the yield of biphenyl is very low in these 0.01*M* solution experiments just discussed. Biphenyl is, of course, the most useful synthetic product of these arylations. In synthesis experiments, more concentrated solutions are used, and yields of 40 to 60% biphenyl are produced. However, studies of reaction mechanisms frequently utilize dilute solutions, and only a minor part of the initially formed addition complex may be converted to biphenyl under these conditions.

10.3 REACTION OF SUBSTITUTED PHENYL RADICALS

Table 10-3 gives the relative rates of reaction of a series of substituted phenyl radicals with nitrobenzene, benzene, and toluene. The *p*-nitrophenyl radical attacks these substrates in the order ϕ-CH_3 > ϕ-H > ϕ-NO_2, whereas the rest of the radicals attack nitrobenzene faster than benzene.

PROBLEMS

1. If phenyl radicals from benzoyl peroxide reacted with benzene to form a cyclohexadienyl radical, this radical would be expected to disproportionate, dimerize, abstract hydrogen, and donate hydrogen. Exemplify each of these processes by an equation.

2. Rationalize the fact that the *p*-nitrophenyl radical reacts faster with benzene than with toluene, whereas the reverse is true of the *p*-methylphenyl radical.

3. Give a mechanism for the formation of phenyl benzoate during the decomposition of benzoyl peroxide in benzene.

4. Substituted phenyl radicals can be generated by using X—⟨◯⟩—N═N—Cϕ_3 as a radical source. When 0.10*M* solutions of these compounds are allowed to decompose in a equimolar mixture of toluene and carbon tetrachloride at 60°C, the following results are obtained: the phenyl radical gives a 47% yield of chlorobenzene, an 18% yield of benzene, and a 35% yield of arylation products; the *p*-nitrophenyl radical gives an 8% yield of chloronitrobenzene, a 17% yield of nitrobenzene, and a 75% yield of arylation products.

a. Write all the reactions involved.

b. Explain the difference in behavior between the phenyl and the *p*-nitrophenyl radicals.

11 Radical Rearrangements

Rearrangements of free radicals, although not commonplace, do occur in some systems. Most often a radical rearrangement has only nuisance value and makes the product mixture even more complex than usual. Sometimes, however, radical rearrangements can be utilized in syntheses.

11.1 1,2-ARYL MIGRATIONS

By far the largest number of radical rearrangements are those in which an aryl group moves from one position to the adjacent atom. The radical that undergoes rearrangement can be generated in a number of ways. For example, the treatment of phenylisovaleraldehyde with peroxides gives the following results:

$$\phi-\underset{CH_3}{\overset{CH_3}{\underset{|}{\overset{|}{C}}}}-CH_2-CHO \xrightarrow{\text{initiators}} \underset{\text{I}}{\phi-\underset{CH_3}{\overset{CH_3}{\underset{|}{\overset{|}{C}}}}-\dot{C}H_2}$$

$$\underset{\text{I}}{\phi-\underset{CH_3}{\overset{CH_3}{\underset{|}{\overset{|}{C}}}}-\dot{C}H_2} \xrightarrow{\text{rearrangement}} \cdot\underset{CH_3}{\overset{CH_3}{\underset{|}{\overset{|}{C}}}}-CH_2\phi \xrightarrow[\text{abstraction}]{\text{hydrogen}} \underset{\text{rearranged product}}{H\underset{CH_3}{\overset{CH_3}{\underset{|}{\overset{|}{C}}}}-CH_2\phi} \qquad (11\text{-}1)$$

$$\underset{\text{I}}{\phi-\underset{CH_3}{\overset{CH_3}{\underset{|}{\overset{|}{C}}}}-\dot{C}H_2} \xrightarrow[\text{abstraction}]{\text{hydrogen}} \underset{\text{unrearranged product}}{\phi-\underset{CH_3}{\overset{CH_3}{\underset{|}{\overset{|}{C}}}}-CH_3} \qquad (11\text{-}2)$$

This system is a particularly favorable one for rearrangement because a primary radical rearranges to a more stable tertiary one. In pure aldehyde as solvent, 60% of the hydrocarbon product is of the rearranged structure. Under these conditions, therefore, Reaction (11-1) is slightly faster than (11-2). Notice that if this mechanism is correct, the amount of rearrangement will depend on the concentration of hydrogen donors in the system. In this case, the most active hydrogen donor is the aldehyde itself. Therefore, if the aldehyde concentration is decreased, the rate of Reaction (11-1) should increase relative to Reaction (11-2) and a larger amount of rearrangement should be observed. In agreement with this, the amount of rearrangement increases from 60 to 80% when the aldehyde is diluted to 1 *M* with chlorobenzene as solvent. The addition of a very active hydrogen donor (such as a thiol) should cause I to be converted to unrearranged product even faster, and less rearrangement should be observed. This has been confirmed in related systems.

Cyclic aldehydes may also undergo decarbonylation with rearrangement:

ϕ, CH_2—CHO (cyclopentane) ⟶ ϕ, $\dot{C}H_2$ (cyclopentane) $\xrightarrow{\text{rearrangement}}$ $CH_2\phi$, • (cyclopentane) $\xrightarrow{\text{RCHO}}$ H, $CH_2\phi$ (cyclopentane)

ϕ, CH_2—CHO (cyclohexane) ⟶ ϕ, $\dot{C}H_2$ (cyclohexane) $\xrightarrow{\text{rearrangement}}$ •, $CH_2\phi$ (cyclohexane) $\xrightarrow{\text{RCHO}}$ H, $CH_2\phi$ (cyclohexane)

In the cyclopentyl compound shown above, the extent of rearrangement increases from 63 to 92% when the aldehyde is diluted to 1 *M* with chlorobenzene. The rearrangement decreases to less than 2% if benzyl mercaptan is added; this very active hydrogen donor traps the first radical before it rearranges.

In the above cases, a primary or secondary radical rearranges to a more stable tertiary radical. The rearrangement from one primary radical to another primary radical also occurs in some circumstances. For example, 3-phenylpropanal-2-C-14 rearranges to the extent of 4% at 170°C. The addition of thiophenol reduces the extent of rearrangement, indicating that the mechanism most likely involves radicals:

$$\phi\text{—C—C*—CHO} \xrightarrow[\text{initiators}]{\text{radical}}$$

$$\phi\text{—C—}\dot{C}^{*} \xrightarrow{\text{rearrangement}} \cdot\text{C—}\overset{*}{\text{C}}\text{—}\phi \xrightarrow{\text{RCHO}} \phi\text{—CH}_2^{*}\text{—CH}_3 \quad 4\%$$

$$\phi\text{—C—}\dot{C}^{*} \xrightarrow{\text{RCHO}} \phi\text{—CH}_2\text{—}\overset{*}{\text{C}}\text{H}_3 \quad 96\%$$

Relative rates for the migration of substituted phenyl groups can be obtained by an analysis of the rearrangement of 3-aryl-3-methylbutanaldehydes. The reactions that occur are shown below:

$$p\text{-}X\text{-}C_6H_4\text{-}C(C)(C)\text{-}C\text{-}CHO \xrightarrow{\text{initiators}} p\text{-}X\text{-}C_6H_4\text{-}C(C)(C)\text{-}C\cdot$$

$$p\text{-}X\text{-}C_6H_4\text{-}C(C)(C)\text{-}C\cdot \xrightarrow[k_1]{\text{RCHO}} p\text{-}X\text{-}C_6H_4\text{-}C(C)(C)\text{-}C \tag{11-3}$$

$$p\text{-}X\text{-}C_6H_4\text{-}C(C)(C)\text{-}C\cdot \xrightarrow[k_2]{\text{rearrangement}} p\text{-}X\text{-}C_6H_4\text{-}C\text{-}\dot{C}(C)\text{-}C \xrightarrow{\text{RCHO}} p\text{-}X\text{-}C_6H_4\text{-}C\text{-}C(C)\text{-}C \tag{11-4}$$

$(R = Ar—C(CH_3)_2—CH_2)$

Equation (11-5) can be easily obtained:

$$\frac{k_2}{k_1} = \frac{(\%\text{ yield rearranged product})}{(\%\text{ yield unrearranged product})}(\text{RCHO}) \tag{11-5}$$

If the reasonable assumption is made that k_1 is a constant and independent of X, then the values of k_2 obtained for different substituents can be compared. The results obtained are:

X	Relative k_2
Cl	1.8
H	1.0
CH_3	0.6
CH_3O	0.35

Note that electron-withdrawing X groups speed the rearrangement.

In the above examples, we have considered radical migrations to carbon atoms. Radicals can also migrate to other atoms. For example, aryl groups can migrate to oxygen in certain alkoxy radicals. The hydroperoxide below rearranges as shown:

$$Ar\text{—}C(\phi)_2\text{—}O\text{—}OH \longrightarrow Ar\text{—}C(\phi)_2\text{—}O\cdot \xrightarrow{\text{rearrangement}} \cdot C(\phi)_2\text{—}O\text{—}Ar \longrightarrow H\text{—}C(\phi)_2\text{—}O\text{—}Ar$$

(Ar = *p*-nitrophenyl)

Note that a *p*-nitrophenyl group migrates in preference to phenyl. In carbonium ion rearrangements, phenyl migrates more easily than does *p*-nitrophenyl.

11.2 1,2-ALKYL AND HYDROGEN MIGRATIONS

There is no unequivocal evidence that 1,2-hydrogen or alkyl group migrations occur in radical reactions. In the few systems where such migrations have been postulated, other more probable paths could also explain the products. It is not unexpected that 1,2-aryl migrations are more common in radical reactions than are 1,2-alkyl or hydrogen migrations; in carbonium ion rearrangements, groups migrate in the order aryl > alkyl or hydrogen.

11.3 1,2-HALOGEN MIGRATIONS

Rearrangement involving halogen atom migration was discussed briefly in Sec. 8-2 in connection with the addition of hydrogen halides to olefins. The addition of hydrogen bromide to halogen-containing olefins frequently leads to rearrangements. An example in which the product is entirely of the rearranged structure is given below.

$$\text{Br}\cdot + \text{C}{=}\text{C}{-}\text{CCl}_3 \longrightarrow \text{Br}{-}\text{C}{-}\dot{\text{C}}{-}\text{CCl}_3$$

$$\text{Br}{-}\text{C}{-}\dot{\text{C}}{-}\text{CCl}_3 \xrightarrow{\text{rearrangement}} \text{Br}{-}\text{C}{-}\underset{\text{Cl}}{\underset{|}{\text{C}}}{-}\dot{\text{C}}\text{Cl}_2$$

$$\text{Br}{-}\text{C}{-}\underset{\text{Cl}}{\underset{|}{\text{C}}}{-}\dot{\text{C}}\text{Cl}_2 + \text{HBr} \longrightarrow \text{BrCH}_2{-}\underset{\text{Cl}}{\underset{|}{\text{CH}}}{-}\text{CHCl}_2 + \text{Br}\cdot$$

This mechanism leads to the prediction that any radical could effect the rearrangement; in accord with this, radical addition of thiols or bromine also leads to rearranged products:

$$\text{C}{=}\text{C}{-}\text{CCl}_3 \xrightarrow{\text{RS}\cdot} \text{RS}{-}\text{C}{-}\dot{\text{C}}{-}\text{CCl}_3 \xrightarrow{\text{rearrangement}}$$

$$\text{RS}{-}\text{C}{-}\underset{\text{Cl}}{\underset{|}{\text{C}}}{-}\dot{\text{C}}\text{Cl}_2 \xrightarrow{\text{RSH}} \text{RS}{-}\text{CH}_2{-}\underset{\text{Cl}}{\underset{|}{\text{CH}}}{-}\text{CHCl}_2$$

$$\text{C}{=}\text{C}{-}\text{CCl}_3 \xrightarrow{\text{Br}\cdot} \text{Br}{-}\text{C}{-}\dot{\text{C}}{-}\text{CCl}_3 \xrightarrow{\text{rearrangement}}$$

$$\text{Br}{-}\text{C}{-}\underset{\text{Cl}}{\underset{|}{\text{C}}}{-}\dot{\text{C}}\text{Cl}_2 \xrightarrow{\text{Br}_2} \text{BrCH}_2{-}\underset{\text{Cl}}{\underset{|}{\text{CH}}}{-}\underset{\text{Br}}{\underset{|}{\text{CCl}_2}}$$

11.4 RING-OPENING AND RING-CLOSING REACTIONS

The peroxide-initiated addition of carbon tetrachloride to β-pinene gives rearranged chloride in high yield:

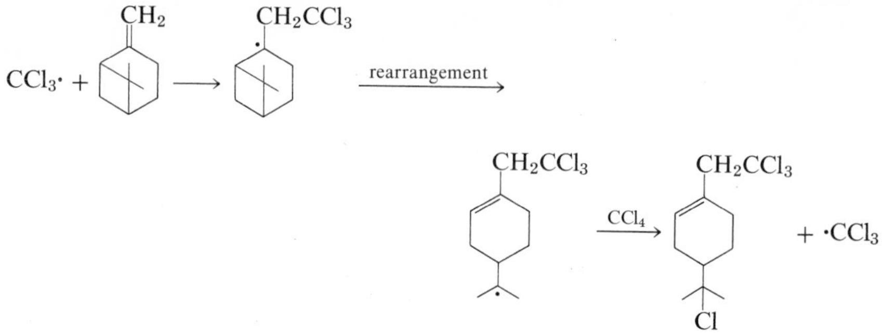

$CCl_3\cdot$ + [β-pinene] ⟶ [radical adduct with CH_2CCl_3] $\xrightarrow{\text{rearrangement}}$ [ring-opened radical with CH_2CCl_3] $\xrightarrow{CCl_4}$ [product with CH_2CCl_3 and Cl] + $\cdot CCl_3$

Thiolacetic acid, however, adds to β-pinene to give mainly unrearranged product. This superior transfer agent traps the first-formed radical. The rearrangement reaction observed with carbon tetrachloride will be recognized as a β-scission, but in a cyclic system this produces rearranged product.

An interesting ring opening reaction is observed during the chlorination of spiropentane:

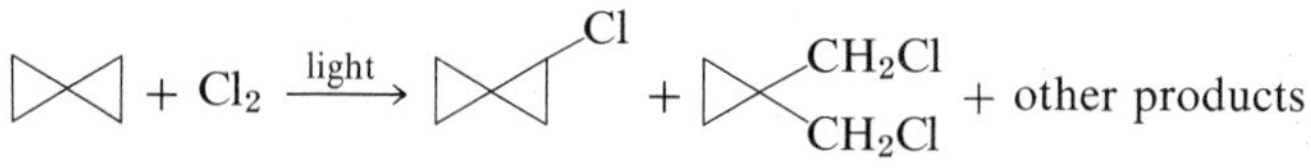

[spiropentane] + Cl_2 $\xrightarrow{\text{light}}$ [chlorospiropentane, Cl] + [cyclopropane with CH_2Cl, CH_2Cl] + other products

The dichloride product could be the result of the radical displacement reaction shown below:

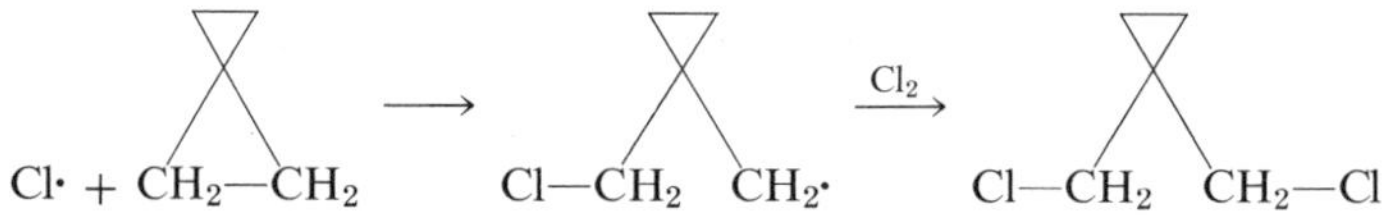

$Cl\cdot$ + CH_2—CH_2 ⟶ Cl—CH_2 $CH_2\cdot$ $\xrightarrow{Cl_2}$ Cl—CH_2 CH_2—Cl

Other systems are known that undergo β-scission reactions to produce ring-opened products. For example, the substituted pyran below rearranges at 125°C in a peroxide-initiated reaction:

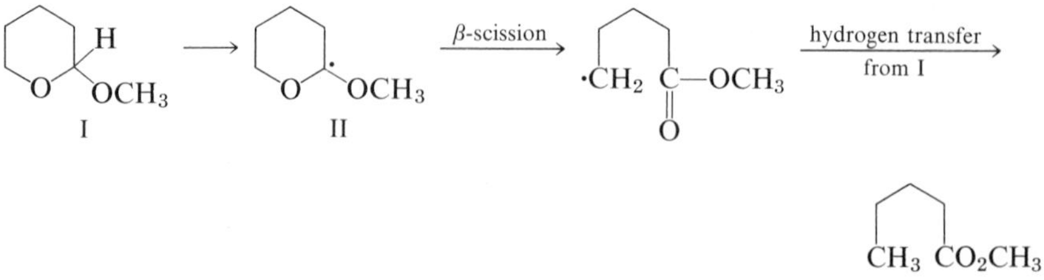

[pyran with H, OCH_3] I ⟶ [radical, OCH_3] II $\xrightarrow{\beta\text{-scission}}$ $\cdot CH_2$ C—OCH_3 (C=O) $\xrightarrow[\text{from I}]{\text{hydrogen transfer}}$ CH_3 CO_2CH_3

Ring closures are the reverse of these ring opening β-scission reactions. One example of such a reaction is the formation of a tricyclic compound by the addition of an aromatic thiol to norbornadiene:

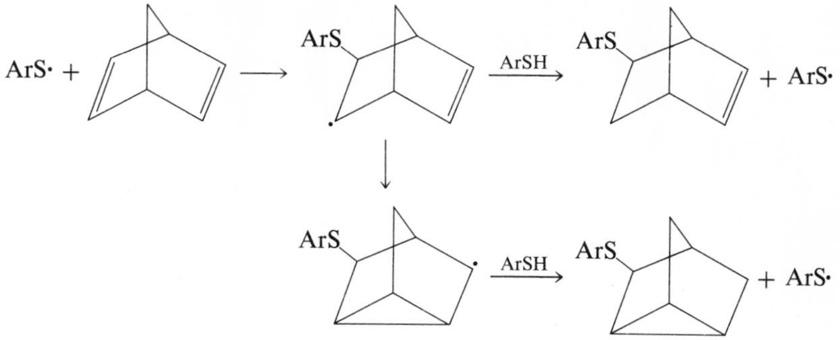

The extent of ring closure was found to decrease as more thiol was added, indicating that the first radical could be trapped by a high concentration of transfer agent.

11.5 1,4- AND 1,5-HYDROGEN MIGRATIONS

Terminal radicals can "bite back" on themselves and abstract a hydrogen from the fourth or fifth carbon down the chain:

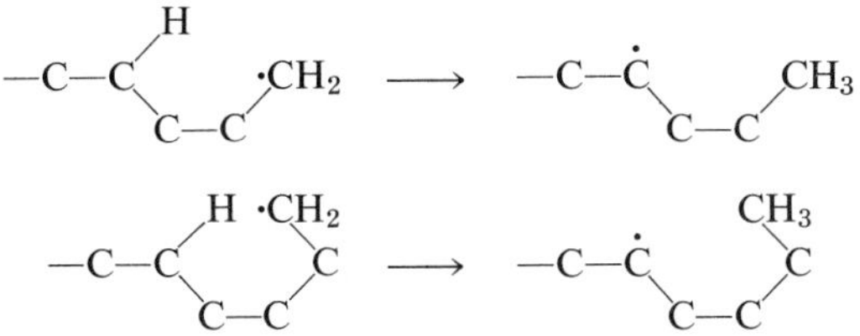

This rearrangement occurs because of the increased stability of a secondary over a primary radical, and the five or six membered quasi-ring transition state provides a low energy path. The reaction is thought to be responsible for the short-chain branches that occur along the polyethylene backbone when the material is prepared by a radical polymerization.

An example of a 1,5-hydrogen transfer that has synthetic utility occurs in the Hofmann-Loffler reaction. In this reaction, an N-haloamine is converted to a pyrrolidine by irradiation in acid solution followed by treatment with base. The mechanism is believed to be as follows:

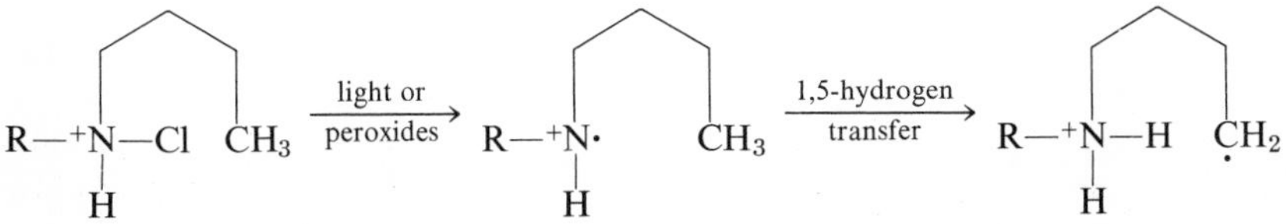

(mechanism continued on next page)

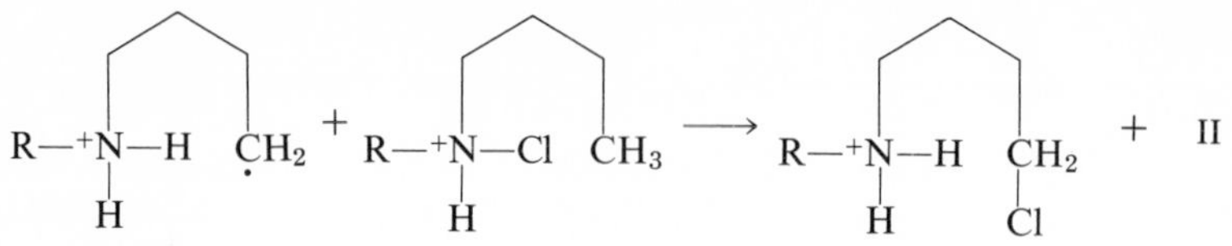

$$\text{R}\!-\!\overset{+}{\text{N}}(\text{H})\!-\!\text{H}\ \ \dot{\text{C}}\text{H}_2\ (\text{III}) + \text{R}\!-\!\overset{+}{\text{N}}(\text{H})\!-\!\text{Cl}\ \ \text{CH}_3\ (\text{I}) \longrightarrow \text{R}\!-\!\overset{+}{\text{N}}(\text{H})\!-\!\text{H}\ \ \text{CH}_2\text{Cl}\ (\text{IV}) + \text{II}$$

The further reaction of compound IV with base produces the pyrrolidine:

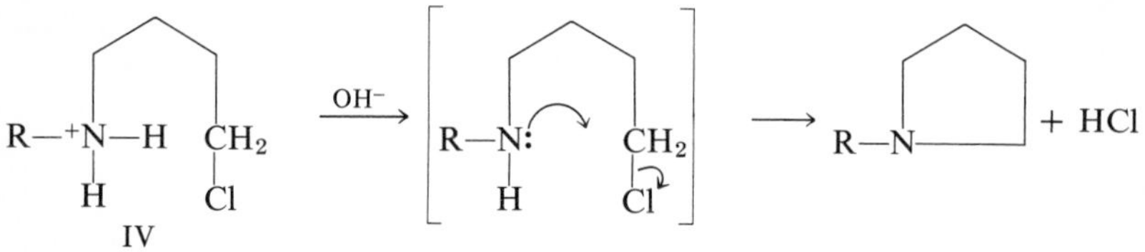

$$\text{R}\!-\!\overset{+}{\text{N}}(\text{H})\!-\!\text{H}\ \ \text{CH}_2\text{Cl}\ (\text{IV}) \xrightarrow{\text{OH}^-} \left[\text{R}\!-\!\ddot{\text{N}}(\text{H})\ \ \text{CH}_2\text{—Cl}\right] \longrightarrow \text{R—N(pyrrolidine)} + \text{HCl}$$

PROBLEMS

1. Discuss the evidence that suggests that two open chain radicals exist in the radical decarbonylation of

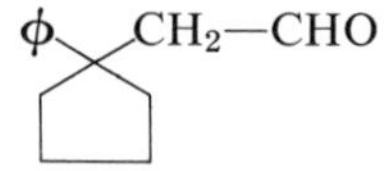

$$\phi\text{, CH}_2\text{—CHO (on cyclopentane)}$$

Would a single bridged radical (in which phenyl bridges as the CO leaves) explain the data equally well?

2. Explain the effect of substituents on the rearrangement of 3-aryl-3-methyl-butanal (p. 100).

3. Give all the possible hydrocarbon products, both rearranged and unrearranged, from the decomposition of the azo compound shown below:

$$\phi(\text{CH}_3)_2\text{C—CH(CH}_3\text{)—N=N—CH(CH}_3\text{)—C(CH}_3)_2\phi$$

4. Suggest an explanation for the *p*-nitrophenyl migrating in preference to phenyl in the alkoxy radical shown below:

$$p\text{-NO}_2\text{—C}_6\text{H}_4\text{—C}\phi_2\text{—O}\cdot$$

(Draw the transition states for both processes, and discuss their relative energetics.)

5. Explain the difference between the reactions in Section 11.3 (p. 101) where rearrangements occur, and those in Section 8.2 (p. 78) where rearrangements do not occur.

12 Termination Reactions

12.1 INTRODUCTION

We can conclude our study of radicals by a consideration of some of the features of the processes which end chains. Termination reactions occur in every radical system. In fact, one of the most characteristic features of radical species is that they react in pairs; neither carbonium ions nor carbanions show this pairing tendency.

Alkyl radicals can terminate in two ways: by combination and by disproportionation. Combination is simply the reverse of dissociation:

$$2R\cdot \longrightarrow R{-}R$$

In disproportionation, a hydrogen atom that is β to a carbon bearing an odd electron is transferred:

$$R\cdot + R_2\overset{\displaystyle H}{\overset{|}{C}}{-}\dot{C}R_2 \longrightarrow R{-}H + R_2C{=}CR_2$$

Termination reactions are usually bimolecular. The usual kinetic consequence of bimolecular termination is a rate dependence of the overall process on the square root of the rate of initiation. This results since the steady state assumption equates the square of the radical concentration to the rate of initiation. For example, for the initiation and termination steps,

$$\text{initiator} \xrightarrow{R_i} 2R\cdot$$
$$2R\cdot \xrightarrow{k_t} \text{non-radical products}$$

The steady state hypothesis gives

$$R_i = 2k_t(R\cdot)^2$$
$$(R\cdot) = (R_i/2k_t)^{1/2}$$

The rate of the overall process observed usually is proportional to the concentration of radicals, and the total rate of the process, therefore, varies with the square root of the rate of initiation. For example, the rate of polymerization (p. 87) depends on the square root of the concentration of initiator.

12.2 THIRD BODY EFFECT

Since bond-making is exothermic, the combination of two radicals will produce a molecule containing all of the energy of the new covalent bond. In order for this molecule to become stable, it must dissipate this excess energy, either by spreading it throughout its vibrational modes or by collision with a wall or another molecule. Consider the combination of two radicals to form an initially excited species AB*:

$$\text{A}\cdot + \text{B}\cdot \underset{k_2}{\overset{k_1}{\rightleftharpoons}} \text{AB}^* \tag{12-1}$$

$$\text{AB}^* + \text{M} \xrightarrow{k_3} \text{AB} + \text{M} \tag{12-2}$$

where M is an inert third body which deactivates AB* by collision. At the steady state in the excited species AB*, the rate of formation of the stable molecule AB can be written as

$$\frac{d(\text{AB})}{dt} = \frac{k_1 k_3(\text{A}\cdot)(\text{B}\cdot)(\text{M})}{k_2 + k_3(\text{M})}$$

There are two cases: at low concentrations of M, $k_2 \gg k_3(\text{M})$ and the rate of formation of AB equals $\frac{k_1 k_3}{k_2}(\text{A}\cdot)(\text{B}\cdot)(\text{M})$. At high concentrations of M, $k_2 \ll k_3(\text{M})$, and the rate reduces to $k_1(\text{A}\cdot)(\text{B}\cdot)$ and becomes independent of the concentration of the third body. Experimental work has confirmed this "third body" effect for methyl and ethyl radicals and iodine atoms, but larger radicals always follow second order termination rate laws.

12.3 COMBINATION-DISPROPORTIONATION RATIOS

Table 12-1 gives typical data for the ratio of the rate constants for disproportionation to combination for aliphatic radicals in the gas phase. Combination is favored for unbranched radicals, but disproportionation becomes more important as the radical becomes more branched. In general, radicals that have larger numbers of β-hydrogens have larger k_d/k_c ratios, where k_d is the rate constant for disproportionation and k_c the one for combination. Notice that much more disproportionation occurs in branched radicals than could be explained by a statistical effect. For example, the isopropyl radical has twice as many β-hydrogens as does the ethyl radical (i.e., six versus three), but has a five-fold larger k_d/k_c ratio. Similarly, *t*-butyl has nine β-hydrogens and ethyl has three; statistically, therefore, *t*-butyl should have a k_d/k_c ratio that is threefold larger. Actually it is 46 times larger. The discrepancy in every case could be explained by assuming that the absolute rate constant for combination becomes smaller as the radical becomes more hindered through branching. This would amount to postulating a steric strain due to the compression necessary for forming a bond in the combination reaction. It is known that methyl radicals undergo termination with zero activation energy, whereas ethyl radicals require about 2.0 kcal/mole, and triphenylmethyl radicals have an activation energy of about 8 kcal/mole for termination.

Table 12-1

DISPROPORTIONATION/COMBINATION RATIOS FOR RADICALS

Radicals	k_d/k_c
$CH_3\cdot + \cdot C_2H_5$	0.04
$CH_3\cdot + CH_3—CH_2—\dot{C}H_2$	0.03
$2CH_3—\dot{C}H_2$	0.1
$2CH_3—CH_2—\dot{C}H_2$	0.1
$2CH_3—\dot{C}H—CH_3$	0.5
$2(CH_3)_2CH—\dot{C}H_2$	0.4
$2CH_3—CH_2—\dot{C}H—CH_3$	2.3
$2(CH_3)_3C\cdot$	4.6

Most polymeric free radicals terminate predominantly or entirely by combination and their k_d/k_c ratio is very small. The polymeric radical from methyl methacrylate, however, undergoes termination by both mechanisms. The activation energy for disproportionation is about 5 kcal/mole larger than that for combination, and the fraction of termination by disproportionation therefore increases with increasing temperature; at 60°C, k_d/k_c is about 1.5.

The rate constants for combination reactions are so large that the rate of termination in the liquid phase can become diffusion-controlled; that is, the diffusion of two radicals through the solution to meet each other is the slow process, and bond formation occurs as soon as the two radicals meet. Under such conditions, the termination rates vary with the nature of the solvent and, especially, with its viscosity. One very dramatic illustration of this is the so-called Trommsdorff effect: the rate of polymerization of certain monomers is observed to increase as the per cent reaction increases. As the reaction solution contains more and more polymer, the viscosity increases and the rate of termination decreases. The rate of polymerization, which is proportional to $k_p/k_t^{1/2}$, therefore increases.

PROBLEM

1. Two values of k_d/k_c can be measured for the reaction between ethyl and propyl radicals, since either ethylene or propylene can be formed in the disproportionation:

$$C_2H_5\cdot + \cdot C_3H_7 \xrightarrow{k_c} C_5H_{12}$$

$$C_2H_5\cdot + \cdot C_3H_7 \xrightarrow{k_{d(e)}} H_2C{=}CH_2 + C_3H_8$$

$$C_2H_5\cdot + \cdot C_3H_7 \xrightarrow{k_{d(p)}} H_2C{=}CH—CH_3 + C_2H_6$$

It is found that $k_{d(p)}/k_c = 0.081$. Compare this value with others in Table 12.1. Is it reasonable? Predict an approximate value for $k_{d(e)}/k_c$.

Index

Acetyl peroxide, 20, 23, 24
Activation energy, 9
Addition polymerization, 82
Addition reactions, 3, 70ff
AIBN, 28
Alkyl peroxides, mechanisms of decomposition, 19, 21
Apocamphoyl peroxide, 16
Aromatic substitution, 92ff
Atom-transfer reactions, 3
Azo compounds, 27–30
Azoisobutyronitrile (*see* AIBN)

Benzoyl peroxide, 20, 24–25, 34, 72, 93–96
Bond dissociation energy, 9, 33
Bridged radicals, 16, 75
Bromination, 65
  of optically active materials, 15
Bromine atoms, 56
N-Bromosuccinimide, 67–69
t-Butoxy radical, 10, 22, 56
t-Butyl hydroperoxide, 30, 32
t-Butyl hypochlorite, 55, 64–67, 69
t-Butyl peracetate, 48
t-Butyl perbenzoate, 20
t-Butyl peroxide, 9, 10, 20–21, 55

Cage reaction, 23, 29, 96
Carbon tetrabromide, as addend, 73
Carbon tetrachloride, as addend, 78–79
Chain transfer, 87
Chlorination, 3, 59, 62–65, 69
  of optically active materials, 14
  photo-initiated, 40
Chlorine atoms, 56–57
Combination, 105–107
Condensation polymerization, 82
Copolymerization, 89ff
Copolymers, 85
Copper-catalyzed perester reactions, 48
Cumene hydroperoxide, 47

Dialkyl peroxides, 19, 21
Diphenylpicrylhydrazyl, 7, 8
Disproportionation, 105–107
Disulfides, as transfer agents, 89
DPPH, 7, 8, 28

Electron paramagnetic resonance, 5, 6
Energy transfer, 38, 43
Epr (*see* Electron paramagnetic resonance)

Fenton's reagent, 47
Fluorescence, 38
Fluorination, 61
Fragmentation reactions, 4
Free radical (*see specific radicals, e.g.*, Methyl radical, *etc.*)

Gomberg reaction, 93

Hammond principle, 53
Heat of formation, 10
Heat of reaction, 8
Hofmann-Loffler reaction, 103
Hydrogen abstraction, 51ff
  by chlorine atoms, 52
Hydrogen bromide, addition to olefins, 73–78
  stereochemistry of addition, 74
Hydrogen peroxide, 30, 47
Hydrogen sulfide, as addend, 79, 80

Induced decomposition, 19, 96
Intersystem crossing, 39, 43
Iodination, 65
Isomerization of olefins, 72

Kel-F, 84
Kinetics of polymerization, 86ff
Kolbe reaction, 46

Methyl radical, 6, 54, 56, 107
from acetone, 42
Molecule-induced homolysis, 31
in chlorinations, 63
in fluorinations, 62

NBS, 67–69
N-Nitrosoacetanilide, 93, 94

1-Octene, addition to, 78–79
One electron transfer redox reactions, 46ff

Peresters, 25, 26, 32, 47
Phenylazotriphenylmethane, 27, 55, 93
Phenyl radical, 56, 96
Phosphorescence, 38
Photochemistry, 37ff
Polar effects on radical reactions, 57
Polymerization, 70–72, 82ff
Polymers, examples of useful, 83ff
Polyvinyl chloride, 84
Propagation reactions, four types, 3

Radical, optically active, 14
Radicals:
conformation of, 13
hybridization of, 13
Reactivity and its relation to selectivity, 53
Rearrangement reactions, 5
Rearrangements, 77, 98ff
1,2-aryl migrations, 98ff
1,2-halogen migrations, 101
Rearrangements (*cont.*):
1,4- and 1,5-hydrogen migrations, 103f
Redox reactions, 46ff

Saran, 85
β-Scission, 4
leading to rearrangements, 101, 102
Selectivity and its relation to reactivity, 53
Singlet species, 39
Solvent effects on radical reactions, 58
Steady-state approximation, 86, 87
Styrene, 32, 72, 79, 85, 88
in copolymerizations, 90

Teflon, 84
Telomer, 70
Thiol, as transfer agent, 30, 79
Third body effect, 106
Transfer agent, 71
definition, 3
Transfer constant, 72, 88
Transfer reaction, definition, 2
Triphenylbismuth, 94
Triphenylmethyl radical, 6
Triplet species, 39
Triptoyl peroxide, 17

Unimolecular homolysis, 2, 19

Vinyl acetate, 88
Vinyl chloride, 84